Instruments and automatic test equipment

K F IBRAHIM

Instruments and automatic test equipment

An introductory text book

K.F. Ibrahim

Copublished in the United States with
John Wiley & Sons, Inc., New York

Longman Scientific & Technical,
Longman Group UK Limited,
Longman House, Burnt Mill, Harlow,
Essex CM20 2JE, England
and Associated Companies throughout the world.

Copublished in the United States with
John Wiley & Sons, Inc., 605 Third Avenue, New York, NY 10158

First published 1988

British Library Cataloguing in Publication Data

Ibrahim, K.F.
Instruments and automatic test equipment.
1. Automatic testing equipment.
I. Title.
620′.0044

ISBN 0-582-00337-7

ISBN 0-470-21128-8 (USA only)

Set in AM Comp/Edit Times 10/12

Produced by Longman Group (FE) Limited
Printed in Hong Kong

Contents

To Valerie

Preface

The aim of this book is to provide a sound knowledge of the principles, operation and application of the increasingly complex test instruments and equipments. Block schematic diagrams are employed throughout to back-up the text. Although the major developments in test instruments have taken place in logic state testing and automatic test equipment, analogue type instruments remain in wide use in laboratories and workshops. These instruments, including the irreplaceable oscilloscope, are covered in Chapters 2–4. Logic state testing instruments are dealt with in Chapter 5. An introduction to microprocessor-based systems is provided in Chapter 6. The purpose of this is to acquaint the reader with the basic knowledge of microprocessor systems necessary for understanding the need for, and the operation and use of, logic and signature analysers, which are covered in Chapter 7.

A third of the book (Chapters 9–12) is devoted to Automatic Test Equipment (ATE). For a long time, this new and rapidly developing field has been confined to articles in trade magazines written by practising engineers, whose first concern is to expound the virtues of their products. I have attempted to deal with the subject in a systematic way, avoiding the nauseating clutter of the 'buzz words' of this or that (normally American) manufacturer.

It is estimated that as many as 50 per cent of companies which could use ATE do not. The introduction of low-cost ATE will gradually infiltrate all medium and small companies. Knowledge of ATE operation, application and performance capabilities will thus become not just desirable but essential, for designers as well as test and production engineers. As a topic it is being introduced in craft, technician and post-graduate courses.

The book covers the syllabus for City and Guilds Course 224, Part 3 *Electronic Instruments and Testing* and BTEC levels IV and V in 'measurement and testing'. It is also suitable for post-graduate students reading electronic engineering. The book provides valuable assistance to practising engineers engaged in development and testing. It should also be useful to production managers who have to take decisions on the suitability of test equipment to satisfy the requirements of their production.

K.F. IBRAHIM

1 Some basic definitions

Testing is the process of taking measurements, usually of physical quantities, on a device, component, process, or system, to ascertain the performance of the unit under test. It is also often used to find out whether the unit meets the required specification. When a fault is detected, a sequence of other tests are frequently carried out to diagnose the faulty component or device. Hence testing may be divided into two principal types: product testing and diagnostic testing.

Testing

Throughout the process of production and manufacture, testing is carried out at various stages to ensure that the final product conforms to the specified standards and quality. This type of testing is known as **product testing**, which occurs at all stages of manufacture; from component inspection through printed circuit board testing and up to final system testing. Product testing has two main functions. The first is to discover a faulty item before it goes through to the next stage or before it is despatched to the customer. Such faulty items are often repaired and introduced back into the manufacturing process. A second and more profound purpose of product testing is to detect faults at an early stage so that appropriate modifications to the manufacturing process may be introduced, to prevent such faults occurring in the future. In essence, the purpose of product testing is to remove the necessity of product testing.

In **diagnostic testing**, the testing and measurements are carried out on a product, device or system when the unit malfunctions. Unlike the first type where the tests are carried out on both sound and faulty units, diagnostic testing is carried out on a defective unit with known irregular symptoms. The purpose of diagnostic testing is often to identify a faulty sub-unit or component. Electronic servicing for the maintenance and repair of electronic equipments or systems employs diagnostic testing procedures and methods which may be similar to those used in product testing, but are nonetheless distinct from them.

To carry out both product and diagnostic tests successfully, an understanding of the test instruments is essential. It is also important to have a knowledge of the workings and specification requirements of the product, device or system under test.

Specifications

A *specification* is a detailed description of a product, device, component or system outlining the measurements and tests the unit is expected to meet. Since it explains the performance capabilities of the particular unit, this type of specification is referred to as *performance specification*. Performance specification serves two functions, it:

- allows the buyer or user to choose the most suitable unit to meet his or her requirements;
- provides guidelines within which the manufacturing process is carried out.

In some instances, performance specification may be reached by agreement between the manufacturer and the customer. This gives rise to *customer specification* which the product has to meet. To ensure the product meets the agreed specification, the producer constructs his or her own specification known as *manufacturer specification*. The latter is more strict and normally more wide-ranging than the customer specification in order to introduce a safety element against the tolerances inherent in any manufacturing process. An essential part of manufacturer specification is *test specification* produced by the design engineer to guide the test department in checking that the product performance falls within the agreed specification.

British Standards

When specifications are drawn up by the customer or manufacturer, it is normal to quote standard specifications; for example, those produced by the British Standards Institute (BSI), commonly known as *British Standards*. The BSI is the recognized body for the preparation and publication of UK engineering standards. Every year a complete list is published in the British Standards Yearbook.

Automatic testing

With the increasing complexity of electronic circuits, testing has itself become a complex technology forming a very important aspect of all stages of the production process including design, manufacture and field maintenance. Because of this complexity, testing and fault diagnosis can be costly, both in time and money. It is to overcome this that Automatic Test Equipments have been introduced whereby testing procedures, analysis and conclusions are carried out with little or no necessity for intervention of skilled labour. Automatic Test Equipment (ATE) and Systems (ATS) have been manufactured to meet the variety of needs of industry.

2 Analogue-type test instruments

Traditionally, test instruments have been those used to measure analogue or continuously varying quantities, such as voltage, temperature or pressure. Analogue quantities may be measured employing either analogue or digital electronic circuitry. Examples of instruments using analogue circuitry are the moving-coil meter and the Cathode Ray Oscilloscope — where the output is an analogue readout, e.g. a pointer and scale. The Digital Voltmeter (DVM) on the other hand is an example of the digital type employing digital circuitry with a digital display as the output readout. With the advance of digital electronics, new types of instruments had to be developed to measure logic states '0' or '1'. Examples of logic testing instruments are the logic probe, the logic analyser and the signature analyser.

Test instruments may thus be divided into three categories:

the analogue type with analogue readout;
the digital type with digital readout;
the logic state type with a logic 0 or logic 1 readout.

This chapter considers the analogue-type instruments.

The Basic Instrument

Figure 2.1 shows a block diagram for one type of analogue instrument. The transducer converts a non-electrical quantity into an electrical signal. The transducer is thus required only if the input (the quantity to be measured) is non-electrical, e.g. temperature. An electronic circuit may be used to amplify or shape the electrical signal before it is fed into the indicating device to give a reading.

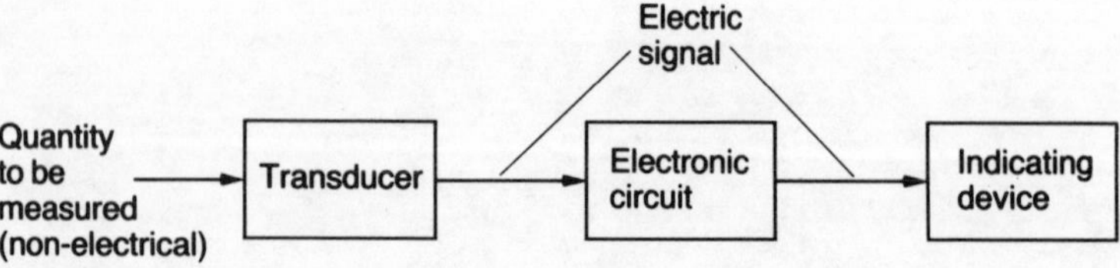

Fig. 2.1 A basic analogue-type instrument

The moving-coil indicator

The moving-coil indicating device is the most popular analogue indicator. It is based on the principle that a current-carrying conductor experiences a force when placed in a magnetic field. Given a magnetic field produced by a permanent magnet, the direction of the force is determined by the direction of current flow, while the strength of the force is determined by the value of the current.

The basic construction of the moving-coil indicating meter is shown in Fig. 2.2. It consists of a coil wound round a soft iron cylindrical core placed within a magnetic field. The magnetic field is produced by a permanent magnet as shown. The coil is pivoted in the centre and mounted in a jewel setting to allow it to rotate freely, hence the name 'moving coil'. A pointer attached to the moving coil indicates on a scale the coil deflection.

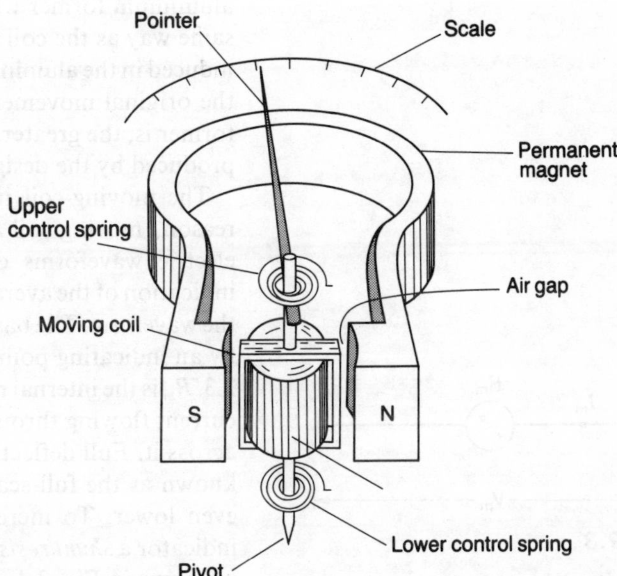

Fig. 2.2 Construction of a moving-coil meter

When direct current flows through the coil, a force is produced which rotates the coil in a direction determined by the direction of the current. However, this movement does not give any indication of the value of the current through the coil. To measure the current, a balancing or controlling torque must be introduced so that the deflection will be proportional to the strength of the rotating force, i.e. the magnitude of the current. This controlling torque is produced by a hair spring which counter-balances the deflecting force so that the pointer settles at an appropriate deflection.

The deflecting torque is proportional to the product of the current through the coil and the magnetic flux density in the air gap between the magnet and the former. The air gap is designed so that the flux density is constant over the range of coil movement giving a deflection torque that is directly proportional to the current. Since the controlling or balancing torque produced by the hair spring is itself proportional to the angle of rotation, the deflection and controlling torques are equal, then the deflection of the former is directly proportional to the current. The angle of deflection is calibrated in appropriate readings on the scale to provide a direct measurement of the current.

Damping of the movement of the meter is necessary to avoid the pointer oscillating above and below its mean value before it settles to its final position. The amount of damping has to be such as to allow the pointer to settle down quickly to a reading following one or two very small oscillations only. This type of damping is known as *critical damping*. The most popular method of damping used in moving-coil meters is the *eddy-current* damping. It consists of an aluminium former which moves within the magnetic field in the same way as the coil. This movement causes eddy currents to be induced in the aluminium former which produces a force opposing the original movement. The more rapidly the movement of the former is, the greater is the force opposing it. Critical damping is produced by the design of the shape of the aluminium former.

The moving-coil indicator measures direct current. For this reason, moving-coil instruments show polarity markings. For electric waveforms other than d.c. the moving coil gives an indication of the average or mean value, i.e. the d.c. component of the waveform. The basic moving-coil indicator may be represented by an indicating pointer having a resistance R_m as shown in Fig. 2.3. R_m is the internal resistance of the moving-coil indicator, I_m the current flowing through the meter and V_m the voltage developed across it. Full deflection of the pointer is produced by a current known as the full-scale deflection current I_f, typically 50 μA or even lower. To increase the current range of the moving-coil indicator a *shunt resistor* R_{sh} is connected in parallel with the coil, as shown in Fig. 2.4.

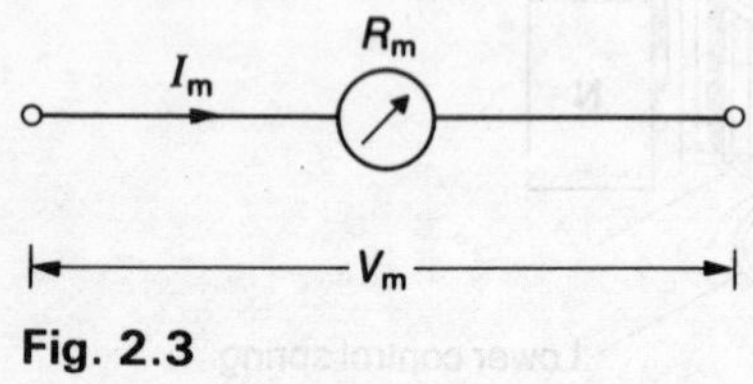

Fig. 2.3

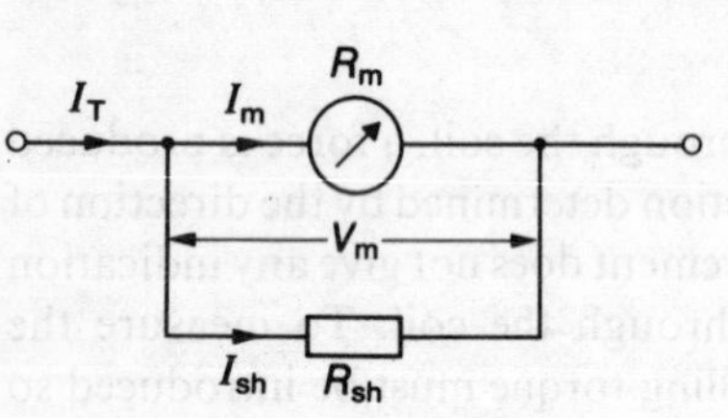

Fig. 2.4 The use of shunt resistor R_{sh}

The voltage drop across the meter $V_m = I_m \times R_m$. Since the shunt resistor R_{sh} is connected in parallel with the meter, the voltage across R_{sh} is also V_m. That is,

$$V_{sh} = V_m$$

Total current $I_T = I_m + I_{sh}$, giving

$$I_{sh} = I_T - I_m$$

and $I_{sh} = \dfrac{V_{sh}}{R_{sh}} = \dfrac{V_m}{R_{sh}}$, giving

$$R_{sh} = \frac{V_m}{I_{sh}}$$

But $V_m = I_m \times R_m$, therefore

$$R_{sh} = \frac{I_m \times R_m}{I_{sh}} = \frac{I_m}{I_{sh}} \times R_m$$

Moreover, $I_{sh} = I_T - I_m$, therefore

$$R_{sh} = \frac{I_m}{I_T - I_m} \times R_m$$

It can be seen that by putting resistor R_{sh} in parallel with the coil, part of the total current can be diverted away from the indicating device thus increasing the range of the meter. For instance, if $R_{sh} = R_m$ then $I_{sh} = I_m$ and $I_T = I_m + I_{sh} = 2I_m$. The current range has thus been doubled.

Example

A moving-coil indicator with an internal resistance of 100 Ω requires 1 mA current to produce full-scale deflection. Calculate the shunt resistor required to increase the range to 10 mA. Also calculate the resulting total resistance of the meter.

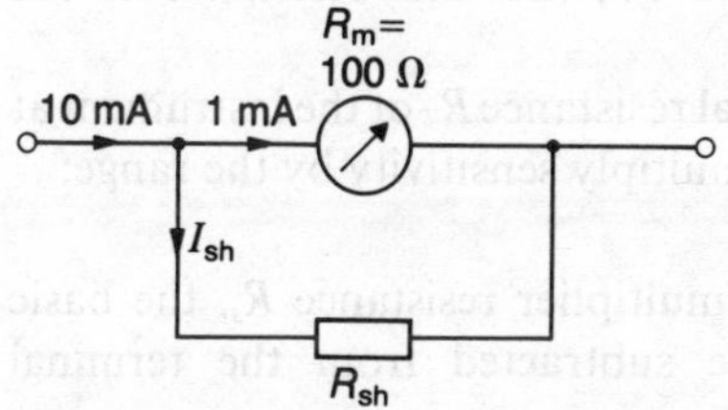

Fig. 2.5

Referring to Fig. 2.5

$$V_m = V_{sh} = I_m \times R_m = 1 \text{ mA} \times 100\ \Omega = 100 \text{ mV}$$

$$I_{sh} = I_T - I_m = 10 \text{ mA} - 1 \text{ mA} = 9 \text{ mA}$$

$$R_{sh} = \frac{V_{sh}}{I_{sh}} = \frac{100 \text{ mV}}{9 \text{ mA}} = 11.1\ \Omega$$

The total resistance of the meter $R_T = \dfrac{V_m}{I_T} = \dfrac{100 \text{ mV}}{10 \text{ mA}} = 10\ \Omega$

Figure 2.6 shows a *multi-range ammeter* with a selector switch. As the switch is moved from one position to another, the value of the shunting resistance is changed, thus changing the full-scale deflection current, i.e. the current range.

The basic moving-coil movement may also be used as a voltmeter. This is achieved by calibrating the scale to read voltage using the fact that full-scale deflection current I_f produces full-scale deflection voltage V_f.

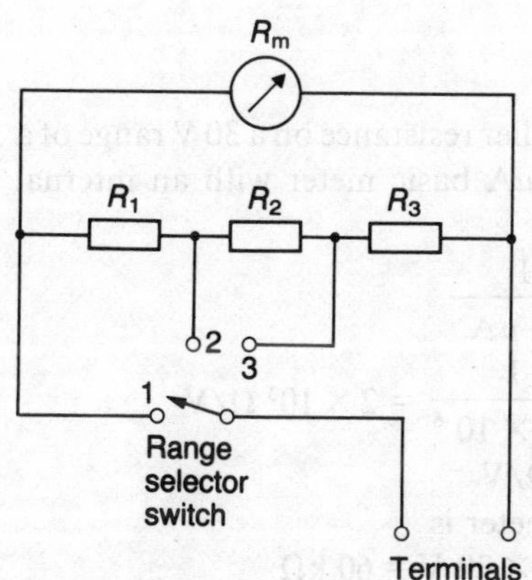

Fig. 2.6 Multi-range ammeter

Assuming $I_f = 50\ \mu$A and $R_m = 100\ \Omega$. Then

$$V_f = I_f \times R_m$$
$$= 50 \times 10^{-6} \times 100$$
$$= 5 \times 10^{-3} \text{ V}$$
$$= 5 \text{ mV}$$

In order to extend the voltage range of the basic meter, a resistor R_s called a *multiplier* is connected in series as shown in Fig. 2.7. The multiplier limits the current through the basic meter to the full-scale deflection current while allowing the terminal voltage V_T to go above the voltage drop across the basic meter V_m. From Fig. 2.7

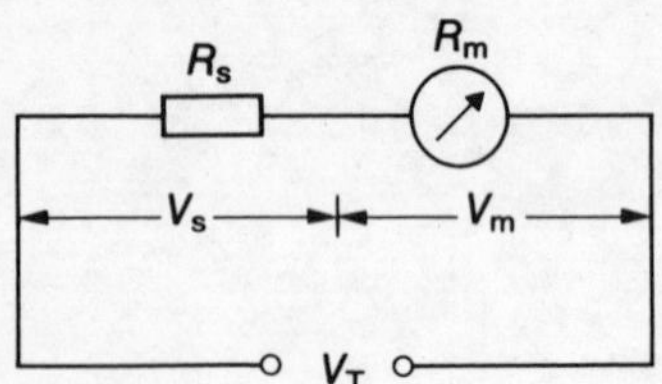

Fig. 2.7 The use of multiplier R_s

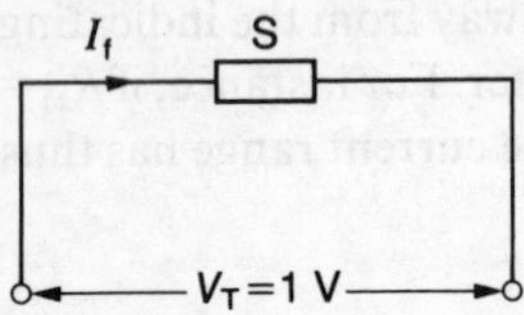

Fig. 2.8

$$V_T = V_m + V_s$$

where V_s is the voltage drop across the multiplier resistor R_s.

Consider the circuit in Fig. 2.8 where a terminal voltage V_T of 1 V is applied across an unknown resistor S causing a current of I_f to flow.

$$\text{resistor } S = \frac{1}{I_f}\ \Omega$$

In the basic meter, S is known as the **sensitivity** of the meter and I_f is the full-scale deflection current. Sensitivity is therefore the reciprocal of full-scale deflection current with a unit of ohms per volt.

$$S = \frac{1}{I_f}\ \Omega/\text{V}$$

It can be seen that sensitivity gives the value of the total resistance of the instrument (multiplier + R_m) for a range of 1V.

For example, given $I_f = 100\ \mu$A, then

$$\text{Sensitivity } S = \frac{1}{100\ \mu\text{A}} = 10 \times 10^3\ \Omega/\text{V} = 10\ \text{k}\Omega/\text{V}$$

In other words, for a range of 1V, the total resistance of the instrument is 10 kΩ.

To calculate the total or terminal resistance R_T of the instrument at ranges other than 1V, simply multiply sensitivity by the range:

$$R_T\ S \times \text{range}\ \Omega$$

To calculate the value of the multiplier resistance R_s, the basic meter resistance R_m must be subtracted from the terminal resistance R_T:

$$R_s = R_T - R_m$$

$$\text{i.e. } R_s = S \times \text{range} - R_m$$

Example

Calculate the value of the multiplier resistance on a 30 V range of a d.c. voltmeter that uses a 500 μA basic meter with an internal resistance of 100 Ω.

$$\text{Sensitivity, } S = \frac{1}{I_f} = \frac{1}{500\ \mu\text{A}}$$

$$= \frac{1}{500 \times 10^{-6}} = 2 \times 10^3\ \Omega/\text{V}$$

$$= 2\ \text{k}\Omega/\text{V}$$

The terminal resistance of the meter is

$$R_T = S \times \text{range} = 2\ (\text{k}\Omega/\text{V}) \times 30\ \text{V} = 60\ \text{k}\Omega$$

$$\therefore \text{multiplier resistance } R_s = R_T - R_m$$

$$= 60\ \text{k}\Omega - 100\ \Omega$$

$$= 60\ \text{k}\Omega - 0.1\ \text{k}\Omega$$

$$= 59.9\ \text{k}\Omega$$

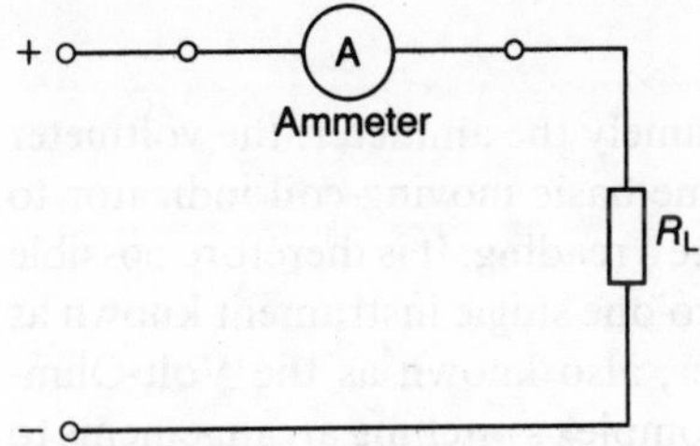

Fig. 2.9

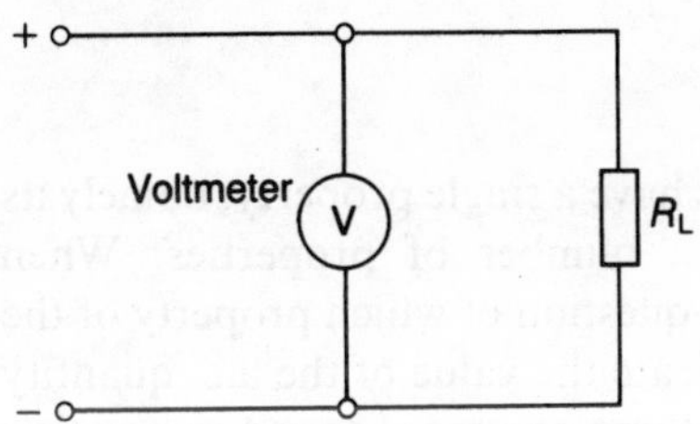

Fig. 2.10

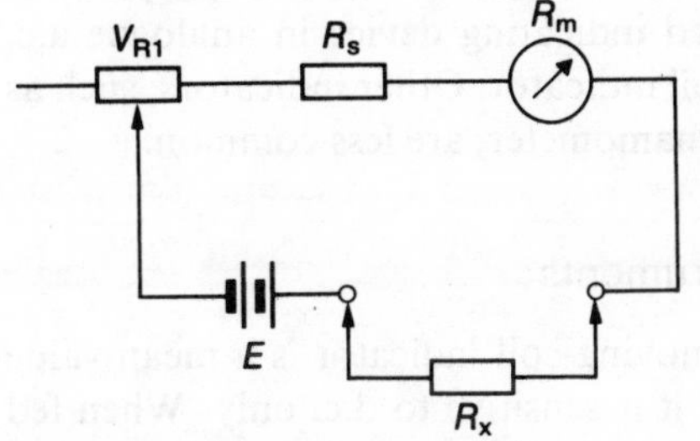

Fig. 2.11 The Ohmmeter

Loading effect of instruments

When an instrument is connected to a circuit, its terminal resistance is added to the resistance of the circuit (in series for an ammeter and in parallel for a voltmeter), thus interfering with the normal function of the circuit. This is known as the *loading effect*. It is desirable to reduce the loading effect to a negligible proportion. If this is not possible, then the loading effect must be taken into account of when interpreting the meter reading when high accuracy is required. For current measurement an ammeter is connected in series with the load (Fig. 2.9). In this case it is essential that the instrument resistance is very low compared with the resistance of the other series components. For voltage measurement a voltmeter is connected in parallel with the load (Fig. 2.10). In this case the instrument resistance must be very high compared with the load resistance.

The ohmmeter

The basic moving-coil meter indicator may be also used in conjunction with a battery to measure resistance. Figure 2.11 shows a simple circuit of an *ohmmeter*. When unknown resistor R_x is connected as shown across two terminals in the circuit, current will flow, producing a deflection. Series resistor R_s is used to limit the maximum current, while VR_1 is used to obtain a zero ohms setting.

Let the total resistance of basic meter, series resistor and the set zero resistor $R_m + R_s + VR_1$ be equal to R_T. Then current through unknown resistor R_X is:

$$I = \frac{\mathrm{E}}{R_T + R_X}$$

By transportation:

$$R_T + R_X = \frac{\mathrm{E}}{\mathrm{I}}$$

$$R_X = \frac{E}{\mathrm{I}} - R_T$$

Thus the relationship between R_X and the current and therefore meter deflection is non-linear, giving a non-linear scale.

The result is a scale being crammed at the higher end and spread out at the lower end. The ohmmeter range may be changed by changing the value of resistor R_s or battery voltage, E.

The multimeter

The three basic instruments, namely the ammeter, the voltmeter and the ohmmeter, use the same basic moving-coil indicator to produce a deflection and indicate a reading. It is therefore possible to combine all three circuits into one single instrument known as the *multimeter*. The multimeter, also known as the Volt-Ohm-Milliammeter (or VOM), uses complex switching arrangements to give the user a choice of units (V, A, Ω) and ranges.

A.C. Measurement

While direct current or voltage have a single property, namely its value, a.c. waveforms have a number of properties. When measuring a.c. waveforms, the question of which property of the waveform is to be used to indicate the value of the a.c. quantity must be answered. There are three commonly used properties: peak, average and r.m.s. (root mean square) values. A.C. voltmeters are available to measure any one of these properties.

The most commonly-used indicating device in analogue a.c. voltmeters is the moving-coil indicator. Other indicators, such as the moving iron and the dynamometer, are less common.

Rectifier moving-coil instruments

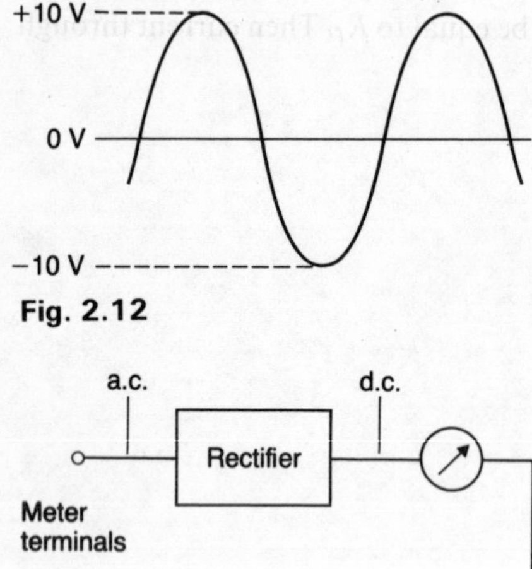

Fig. 2.12

Fig. 2.13 Measuring a.c.

As was stated earlier, the moving-coil indicator is a mean value responding instrument, i.e. it is sensitive to d.c. only. When fed with an a.c. waveform, the indicator will respond to the average or mean value of the waveform. For the sinusoidal waveform shown in Fig. 2.12, the moving-coil indicator will give a zero reading. This is because the d.c. component, i.e. the average or mean value of the waveform, is zero. To use the moving-coil meter to indicate a.c. measurements, the a.c. waveform must first be converted into a suitable d.c. quantity. This is achieved by simple rectification as shown in Fig. 2.13. In this way the indicator will respond to the average or mean of the waveform produced by the rectifier. The usual method of rectification is to use a bridge rectifier, as shown in Fig. 2.14.

If the a.c. input is a sinewave, then the waveform applied to the moving-coil indicator is the full-wave rectified sinewave shown in Fig. 2.15. It has an average (or mean) value $= 0.637 \times$ peak voltage. Assuming the a.c. waveform has a peak voltage of 10 V then a mean value responding meter will indicate a reading of $0.636 \times 10 = 6.36$ V. However, if the meter is required to give direct readings of the R.M.S. values, the measured mean value must be converted to the equivalent r.m.s. value, namely $0.707 \times$ peak voltage. The ratio between the r.m.s. and mean values of a sinusoidal waveform is known as the *form* or *scaling*

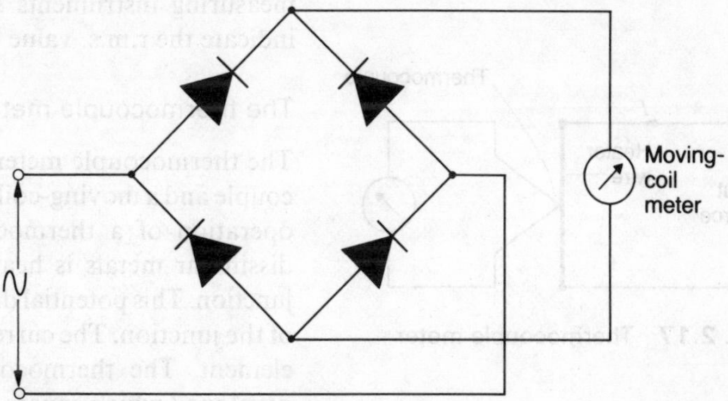

Fig. 2.14 Mean detecting meter

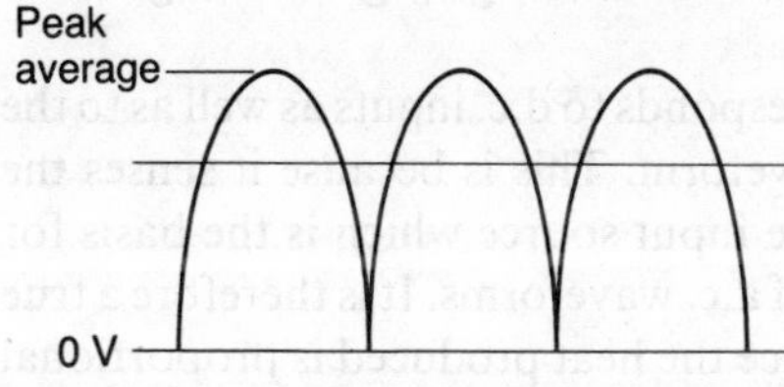

Fig. 2.15

factor. This is the factor which converts mean readings to r.m.s. readings.

$$\text{Form or scaling factor} = \frac{\text{r.m.s. value}}{\text{mean value}}$$

$$= \frac{0.707\ V_p}{0.637\ V_p}$$

$$= \frac{0.707}{0.637} = 1.11$$

When used as r.m.s. value responding instruments, moving-coil meters have their scale calibrated to r.m.s. reading, using the scaling factor of 1.11.

Another technique for measuring a.c. waveforms is the peak detecting method, shown in Fig. 2.16. D_1 is a simple rectifier applying positive half cycles to C_1. Capacitor C_1 charges up to the peak voltage of the a.c. input which is then indicated by the moving-coil meter. Similar to the mean-value responding technique, the scale may be calibrated in r.m.s. values for sinusoidal inputs.

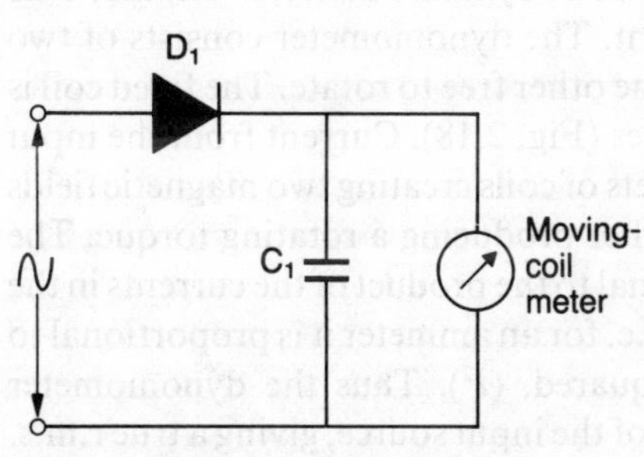

Fig. 2.16 Peak detecting meter

For sinewaves, r.m.s. voltage = 0.707 × peak voltage. The scaling factor in this case is 0.707.

The scaling factors mentioned above are calculated for sinusoidal waveforms only. Other waveforms require different scaling factors depending on their shape. Moving-coil instruments calibrated to indicate r.m.s. values will, therefore, give an incorrect reading if the waveform being measured is non-sinusoidal. This incorrect reading is more pronounced in the peak-value responding method than in the average value.

Moving-coil rectifier meters are therefore not true r.m.s. measuring instruments. They indicate the r.m.s. value for pure sinusoidal waveforms only — as distinct from the true r.m.s.

measuring instruments such as the thermocouple meter which indicate the r.m.s. value of any waveform.

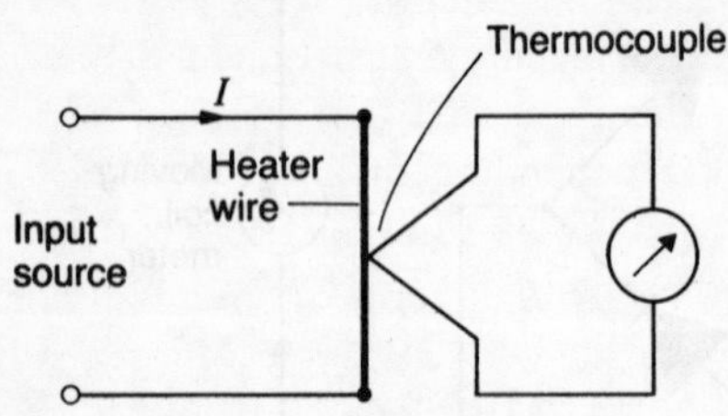

Fig. 2.17 Thermocouple meter

The thermocouple meter

The thermocouple meter consists of a heater element, a thermocouple and a moving-coil indicator (Fig. 2.17). The principle of the operation of a thermocouple is that when a junction of two dissimilar metals is heated, a small e.m.f. is developed at that junction. This potential difference is determined by the temperature of the junction. The current from the input source heats the heater element. The thermocouple senses the heat and an e.m.f. is developed which causes a current to flow giving a reading on the moving-coil indicator.

The thermocouple meter responds to d.c. inputs as well as to the r.m.s. values of any a.c. waveform. This is because it senses the heat energy generated by the input source which is the basis for calculating the r.m.s. value of a.c. waveforms. It is therefore a true r.m.s. responding meter. Since the heat produced is proportional to the square of the current of the input source, the scale of the instrument is non-linear, following a square law, crammed at the low end and spread out at the high end. Its disadvantages are its non-linear scale and slow response time compared with a rectifier type.

The dynomometer

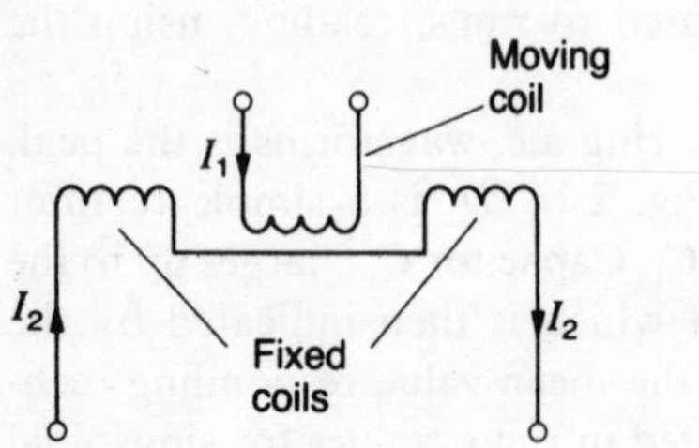

Fig. 2.18 The dynomometer

The dynomometer, or the electrodynamic meter, is another true r.m.s. responding instrument. The dynomometer consists of two sets of coils, one fixed and the other free to rotate. The fixed coil is divided into two equal halves (Fig. 2.18). Current from the input source flows through both sets of coils creating two magnetic fields which interact with each other producing a rotating torque. The rotating torque is proportional to the product of the currents in the fixed and the moving coils, i.e. for an ammeter it is proportional to the value of the current squared, (I^2). Thus the dynomometer responds to the r.m.s. value of the input source, giving a true r.m.s. reading. When used as a voltmeter, the moving and fixed coils are connected in series. When used as an ammeter, the two coils are connected in parallel with each other.

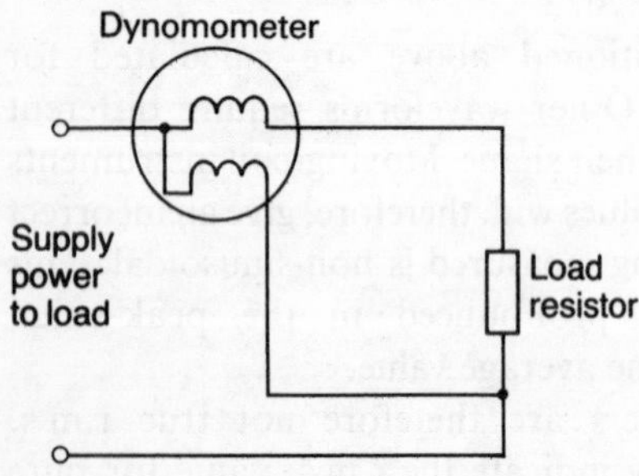

Fig. 2.19 Power measurement

A dynomometer wattmeter may to used to measure power in a load. For this, one coil is connected in series with the load to respond to the load current flow, while the other coil is connected in parallel with the load to respond to the load voltage, as shown in Fig. 2.19. The meter movement will, therefore, be proportional to the product of current and voltage which is the measure of power.

Apart from its use as a power meter, the dynomometer, because of its accuracy, is used as a standard meter for calibrating other instruments.

The Electronic Voltmeter (EVM)

Earlier in this chapter, the volt-ohm-milliammeter (VOM) was considered. This is a rugged and accurate instrument using a moving-coil indicator. It has a sensitivity of 20 000 Ω/V, (a typical input impedance of 10–200 kΩ depending on the range used) and a maximum working frequency of 10 kHz. The electronic voltmeter (EVM), on the other hand, has a very high input impedance, typically 10–100 MΩ which remains constant over all ranges. It also has a greatly improved frequency range of up to 10 MHz or more. Like the VOM, the EVM employs a moving coil to indicate the reading. However, the quantity to be measured is first processed through an amplifier before being fed into the moving-coil indicator.

A *d.c. coupled EVM* consists of an ordinary d.c. moving-coil indicator preceded by a d.c. amplifier of one or more stages (Fig. 2.20). To increase the input impedance, a field effect transistor (fet) is used for the first stage, as shown in Fig. 2.21. The moving-coil indicator responds to the potential difference between points X and Y. With no input, RV_2 is adjusted to make the voltage at Y the same as that at X. Meter current I_1 is therefore zero giving a zero indication. When an unknown input voltage is applied, the current through TR_1 and hence that through TR_2 increases, causing the potential at point X to rise and current I_1 to flow, giving an appropriate indication on the meter. RV_1 is used for calibration purposes.

The d.c. coupled EVM suffers from *drift*, a change of its static conditions over time due to variation in temperature or supply

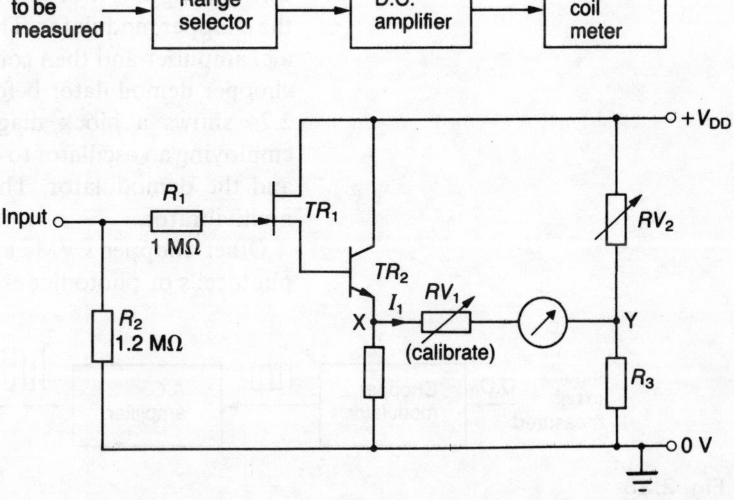

Fig. 2.20 D.C. coupled EVM

Fig. 2.21 Differential amplifier EVM

voltage. Such drift is most noticeable in the zero adjustment. To overcome this, a differential amplifier may be used.

The differential amplifier EVM employs a differential or difference amplifier to detect and measure the unknown input voltage (Fig. 2.22). With no input, points X and Y have equal potential, giving a zero indication. With an unknown input voltage, a potential difference is produced between X and Y, current flows through the meter giving an indication of the voltage. The fets are used to increase the input impedance. The differential amplifier removes drift and improves the common mode rejection of the meter.

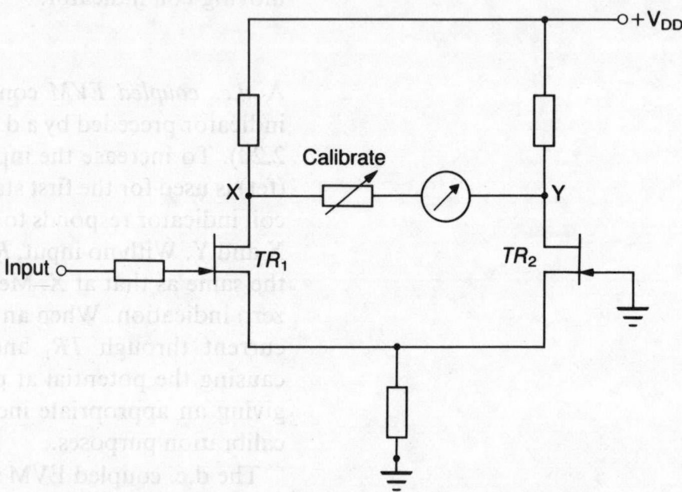

Fig. 2.22

For increased sensitivity (a full scale deflection as low as few μV) and freedom from drift, *a chopper type EVM* is used (Fig. 2.23). The d.c. input is first converted to an a.c. signal (200–300 Hz) by the chopper modulator. The chopped d.c. is amplified by a simple a.c. amplifier and then converted back to d.c. by a synchronized chopper demodulator before it is fed into the voltmeter. Figure 2.24 shows a block diagram for an electronic-type chopper employing an oscillator to control and synchronize the modulator and the demodulator. The oscillator may be a simple astable multivibrator.

Other chopper EVMs use neon-bulb oscillators together with photocells or photodiodes to produce the chopping action.

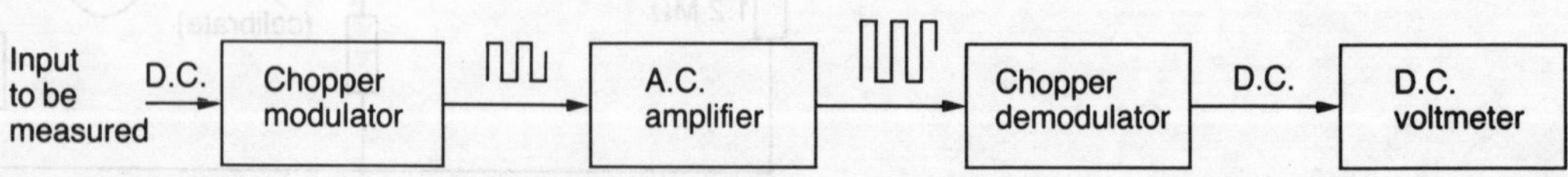

Fig. 2.23

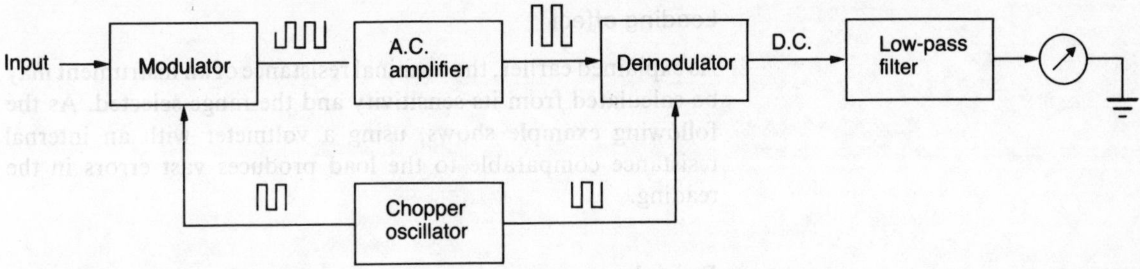

Fig. 2.24 Chopper type EVM

The d.c. EVM considered above may be used for a.c. measurement by first converting the a.c. input into d.c. The rectification may take place before amplification (d.c. mode Fig. 2.25) or after amplification (a.c. mode Fig. 2.26). A high gain amplifier is used with adequate feedback (governed by R_2) for long-term stability.

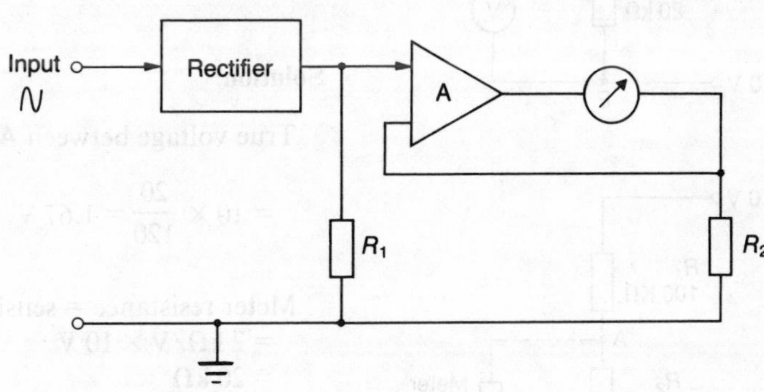

Fig. 2.25 A.C. type EVM (D.C. mode)

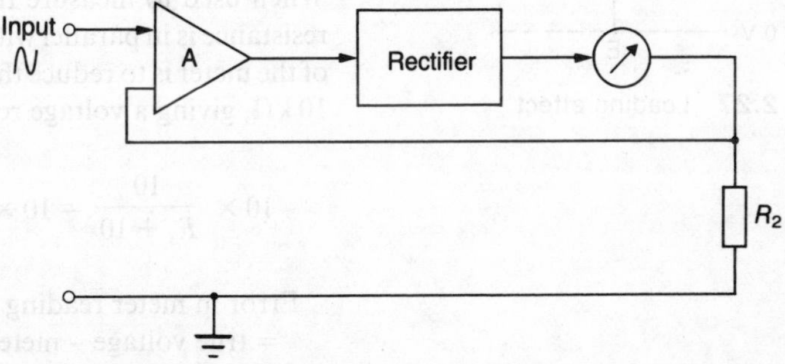

Fig. 2.26 A.C. type EVM (A.C. mode)

Instrument Specification

Every instrument has certain limitations which should be considered when choosing an instrument for a particular measurement. Limitations such as bandwidth, input impedance and accuracy are given by the manufacturer as part of the specification for the instrument. Some of the principal limitations are listed below.

Loading effect

As explained earlier, the terminal resistance of an instrument may be calculated from its sensitivity and the range selected. As the following example shows, using a voltmeter with an internal resistance comparable to the load produces vast errors in the reading.

Example

Consider the simple potential divider circuit shown in Fig. 2.27(a). A voltmeter with a sensitivity of 2 kΩ/V is used to measure the voltage between A and E. When the meter is set to the 10 V range, calculate:

(a) the meter reading,
(b) the error.

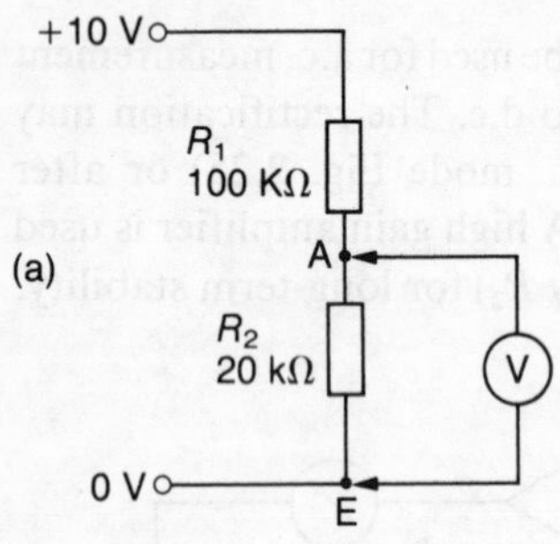

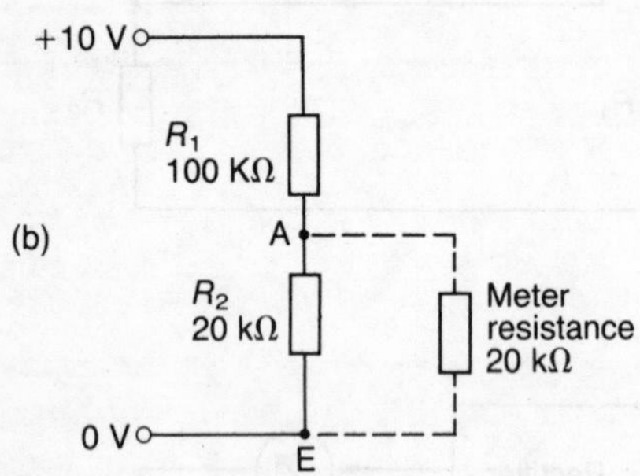

Fig. 2.27 Loading effect

Solution:

True voltage between A and E, $V_{AE} = 10 \times \dfrac{R_2}{R_1 + R_2}$

$$= 10 \times \frac{20}{120} = 1.67 \text{ V}$$

Meter resistance = sensitivity × range
= 2 kΩ/V × 10 V
= 20 kΩ

When used to measure the voltage between A and E, the meter resistance is in parallel with R_2, as shown in Fig. 2.27(b). The effect of the meter is to reduce the effective resistance between A and E to 10 kΩ, giving a voltage reading on the meter of:

$$10 \times \frac{10}{R_1 + 10} = 10 \times \frac{10}{110} = 0.909 \text{ V}$$

Error in meter reading
= true voltage – meter reading
= 1.67 – 0.909
= 0.761 V

A percentage error of $\dfrac{0.761}{1.67} \times 100 = 45.6\%$

Bandwidth

The bandwidth of an instrument states the range of frequency over which the instrument may be suitable. The bandwidth is given as the 3dB points of the frequency response curve of the instrument.

Accuracy

Accuracy is the difference between the instrument reading and the true value. Accuracy is specified as a percentage of the full-scale deflection, i.e. the range of the instrument.

$$\text{Accuracy} = \frac{\text{Reading} - \text{True value}}{\text{Full-scale deflection value}} \times 100\%$$

$$= \frac{\text{Error}}{\text{Range}} \times 100\%$$

For example, a voltmeter with an accuracy of $\pm 1\%$ and a range of 0–100 V should have a maximum error of

$$\mp 1\% \times 100\ \text{V} = \mp 0.01 \times 100\ \text{V} = \mp 1\ \text{V}$$

anywhere over that range. Thus, when measuring a true value of 100 V, the meter may read between 99–101 V. On the other hand, when used to measure a true value of 10 V, the meter reading could be between 9–11 V, a much larger percentage error. Readings are, therefore, more accurate when the instrument deflection is near to its full-scale value. For this reason, it is customary to limit the use of the scale to the upper half or two-thirds by adding ranges in the ratio of 1–2–5 or 1–3–10.

Precision

Precision of an instrument describes how accurately the scale may be read, e.g. up to 0.1 V or 0.001 V. There is no direct relationship between accuracy and precision. An instrument with high precision is not necessarily one that is very accurate.

Resolution

Resolution of an instrument states the smallest change in the input quantity which can be observed in the indicator. Resolution therefore depends on the range selected. For example, on a typical voltmeter, the 10 V range may have a resolution of 5 mV, whereas the 2 V range may have a resolution of 1 mV.

A comparison of typical items found in a typical instrument specification for various types of instruments is given in the table below.

Comparison	*Types of Instrument*				
	Moving Coil (VOM)		EVM	Thermocouple	Dynomometer
Specification	d.c.	a.c.	–	–	–
Accuracy	∓ 1%	∓ 2.5%	∓ 1 – 2.5%	∓ 0.5 – 2.5%	∓ 0.5%
Sensitivity	20 kΩ/V on all ranges	low (1 kΩ/V on all ranges)	very high (10 MΩ or higher)	100 kΩ/V	low (200 Ω/V)
Bandwidth	d.c.	up to 10 kHz	20Hz – 10 MHz or better	Up to 100 MHz or better	Narrow (25 Hz – 100 Hz)
Scale shape	linear	linear	linear	square law	square law
Other remarks	–	Mean – value responding	Mean – value responding	True r.m.s. Slow speed	True r.m.s.

3 Digital-type test instruments

Digital-type meters are those instruments which measure analogue quantities using digital methods and circuitry, with a numerical readout. Examples of digital meters are the digital voltmeter (DVM), the digital multimeter (DMM) and the digital counter.

Comparison of Digital with Analogue Meters

Digital meters have the following advantages over analogue meters:

1. **Readability** The numerical display eliminates parallax error and reduces the possibility of human error associated with analogue readouts. Parallax is an error associated with the pointer-and-scale type indicator. It may be introduced when the eye of the observer is not at right angles to the pointer. For this reason, a mirror is normally incorporated behind the pointer. The instrument should be read with the pointer and its mirror image coinciding with each other.
2. **Accuracy** In general, digital meters have better accuracy, readings often being correct to within ∓0.1% of the true value, as compared with the analogue type, which sometimes has errors as large as ∓10% in, say, EVMs.
3. **Improved precision** and **high level of stability.**
4. Many incorporate **automatic polarity** and **over range protection** which reduce training in its use and avoids instrument damage through overload.
5. **Digital data output facility** Many digital instruments provide an output in digital form for direct feed into a computer, or to operate a printer. This is a decisive factor in the choice of a digital meter for use in production test systems, research, development and maintenance.
6. More sophisticated instruments may employ a microprocessor which allows **mathematical manipulation, storage and comparison of readings**, as well as interfacing with other instruments.

The principal disadvantages are as follows:

1. Unlike the basic analogue meter, the digital instrument **requires a d.c. supply** to operate its circuit.
2. When a digital meter takes a measurement, **a ∓ 1 count ambiguity** can exist in the least significant digit (LSD) (i.e. the digit furthest to the right).

   This may result in the LSD fluctuating between two discrete quantities, even if the input to the instrument is perfectly stable. The ∓1 count error (also known as the **quantizing error**) occurs because the output reading can only be discrete quantities, since the counter is unable to indicate a fraction of a pulse.

The digit display

There are several methods by which the readings of a digital instrument may be displayed ranging from the neon tube to the light emitting diode (LED) and the liquid crystal display (LCD). The number of digits displayed is usually between four and eight. A four-digit display gives a maximum indication of 9999, while an eight-digit display gives a maximum indication of 99999999. For cheaper digital meters, a display known as three-and-a-half-digit display is used. In this type, the most significant digits (MSD, the digit on the extreme left) can only display 0 or 1. Thus the maximum indication is 1999.

Digital Meter

Figure 3.1 shows a general block diagram for a digital instrument. The quantity to be measured is fed into the input attenuator which ensures that the input does not overload the converter. The analogue-to-digital converter (ADC) changes the analogue input quantity into a digital quantity in the form of a binary code. The ADC contains a decade counter which produces a binary coded decimal (BCD) output which has to be decoded before it is fed into the 7-segment display.

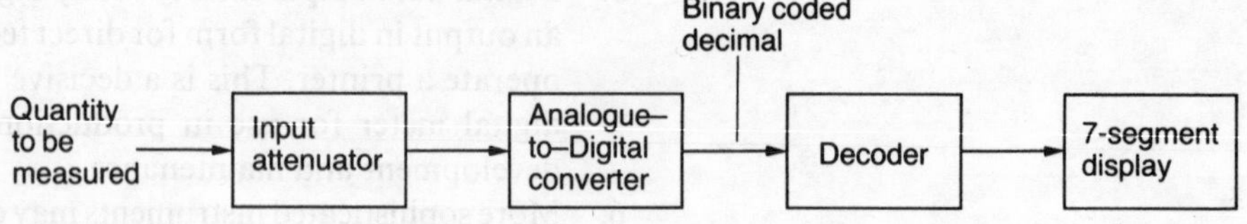

Fig. 3.1 The digital voltmeter, DVM

Display unit

There are two main types of displays: the LED and the LCD. Both consist of seven segments labelled a to g, being the minimum number of segments to represent the decimal numbers from zero to nine as shown in Fig. 3.2. The LCD require very little power to operate, and are used in portable meters. LED displays require more current than LCD and consume more power. They are widely used in bench DVMs, where power consumption is not a primary consideration.

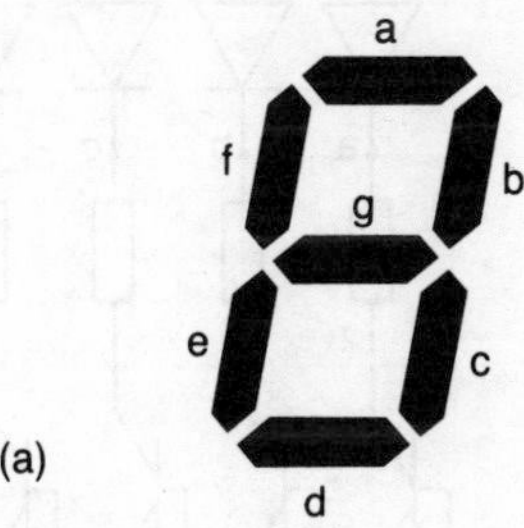

(a)

012345678

(b)

Fig. 3.2 7-segment display

LED drive requirement

Figure 3.3 shows a drive system for one 7-segment LED display. The LED converts electrical current to light. Thus, to illuminate one segment of the display, current must be directed to the diode making up that segment. As shown, one terminal of each diode is connected to a common point. In the example shown, the anodes are connected together making what is known as common-anode configuration. When the cathodes are connected together instead of the anodes, the result is a common-cathode configuration. Each 7-segment display forms one digit of a complete display. Each digit thus has eight terminals; one for each segment and one common connection. In some instances, a decimal point is included in the display, giving a ninth terminal.

Before the segments are driven, the output of, say, a decade counter must be changed into the appropriate signal to drive the display. The output from the counter is in the form of BCD which is four bits of binary information (a bit is an abbreviation of a binary digit). It must be converted into an appropriate signal to drive each of the 7 segments. This conversion is carried out by the decoder.

In practice, the switching driver transistors are contained in a single IC package. Furthermore, the functions of the decoder and

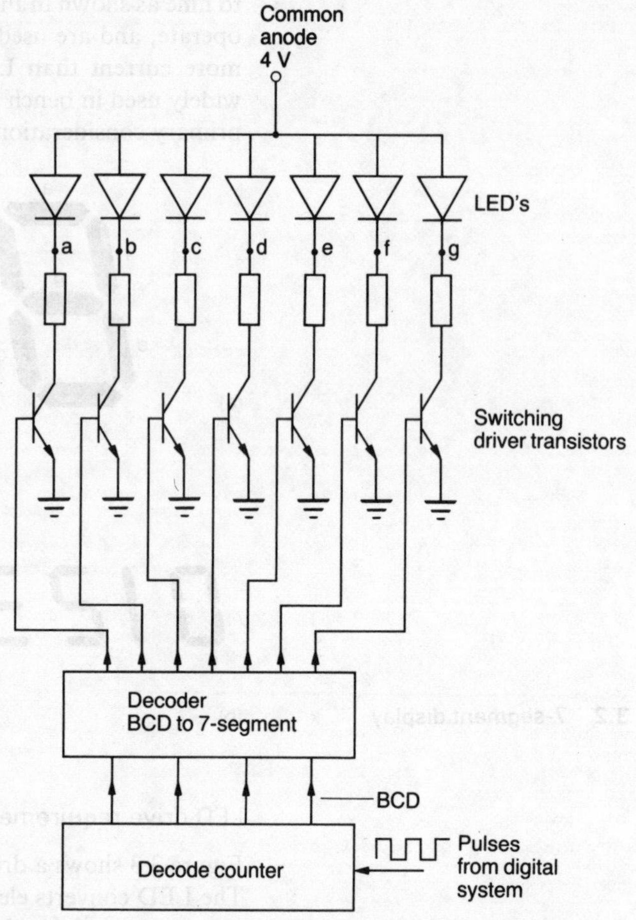

Fig. 3.3 7-segment display drive system

the driver may be performed by a single IC, e.g. the 7447 for common-anode and the 7448 for common-cathode displays. Figure 3.4 shows one such display unit comprising a decade counter, decoder/driver and a common anode 7-segment display.

Latching

A digital meter is essentially a sampling device. Unlike the analogue type, where the input signal is continuously measured, the digital meter takes one sample of the input at a time, processes it through the converter and displays the result. This is then followed by another sample and so on. The display has to be continuously updated. It is important that in the updating process, the display is not turned off, thus causing flicker. To ensure a continuous display, a latch or memory is used, which retains the information and hence the display until updated by the next sample. This is usually incorporated in one IC package, e.g. the latch/decoder/driver, 4511.

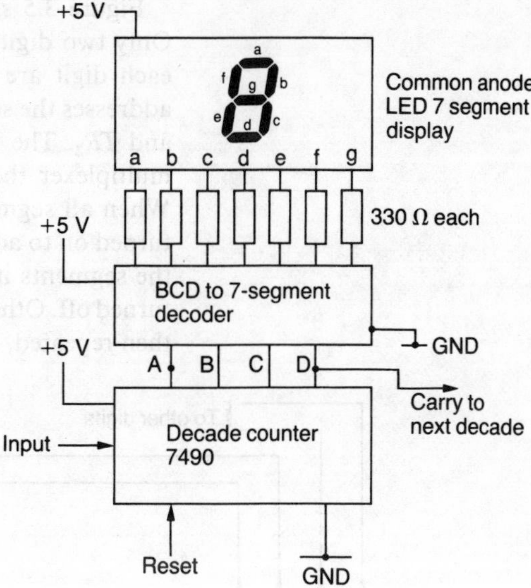

Fig. 3.4

Multiplex drive

The circuit shown in Fig. 3.3 shows that the number of connections necessary for a single digit display is eight (7 segments + a common anode) excluding a decimal point. Normally, more than one digit is necessary, in which case the number of connections is multiplied by the number of digits. For a 4-digit display, the number of connections necessary is $8 \times 4 = 32$. Moreover, a separate drive transistor is also required to drive each segment of the display. Such an arrangement becomes complicated and expensive.

To overcome these problems, use is made of multiplexing or time-sharing technique. Instead of continuously driving each individual LED from a direct supply, the segments are multiplexed, i.e. energized one at a time and in sequence; segment 'a' followed by segment 'b' and so on until segment 'g' and then back to segment 'a' and so on. Provided the frequency of the multiplex is high enough, the brightness of the LEDs will be perceived as continuous by the human eye even though only having an illuminating current passing for one-seventh of the time. This method has a further advantage, specifically related to LED type of displays. By employing a pulse of short duration to drive the LED, the power consumption is greatly reduced, improving efficiency. This is an important aspect of multiplexing LEDs because of their normally high-power consumption when driven from a direct supply. Because of the peculiarities of the human eye, pulsed operation appears to result in greater brightness. Pulses as low as 10% of the direct supply may be used without affecting the average light produced by the LED.

Figure 3.5 shows a multiplexed LED digital display system. Only two digits are shown for simplicity. Identical segments of each digit are connected together in parallel. The multiplexer addresses the segment drivers as well as switching transistors TR_1 and TR_2. The first digit is addressed by switching TR_1 on. The multiplexer then scans the segments in that digit in sequence. When all segments are addressed, TR_1 is turned off and TR_2 is turned on to address the second digit. The multiplexer then scans the segments in the second digit. At the end of the scan, TR_2 is turned off. Other digits are then similarly addressed. The process is then repeated, starting with the first digit.

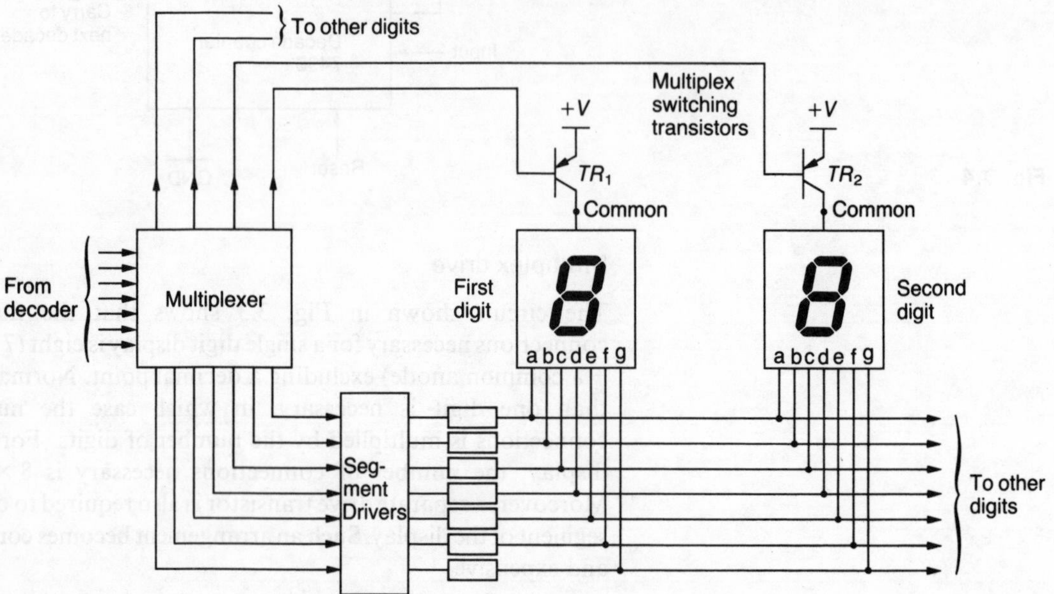

Fig. 3.5 Multiplexing

LCD drive requirements

Liquid crystal displays utilise the unique interaction between electrical and optical characteristics of a family of liquids which retain their crystalline form. They give rise to optical properties which make them important for display operations. Since no light is generated (as is the case with LEDs), the display requires very small currents and consumes little power. Because of this, LCDs may be driven directly by MOS and CMOS circuitry.

LCD devices have two terminals or planes; the front plane (FP) and the back plane (BP). The back planes of all segments are connected in common. Alternating voltages are always used for operating liquid crystal displays in order to avoid electrolytic plating and to ensure maximum life.

The method of driving a liquid crystal display involves feeding a low frequency (typically 40 Hz) square wave to the back plane

(Fig. 3.6(a)). To turn a segment OFF, an in-phase squarewave is fed to the front plane and to turn a segment ON an out-of-phase squarewave is fed to the front plane. When the driving and control waveforms are out of phase, the resultant waveform across the LCD is twice the amplitude of the driving squarewave as shown in Fig. 3.6(b) which turns the segment ON.

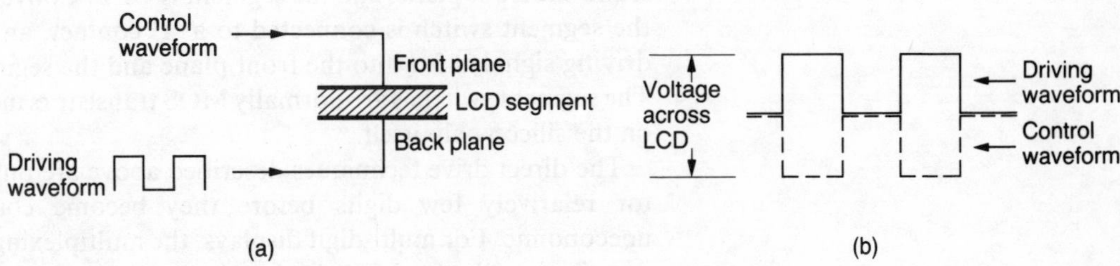

Fig. 3.6 The liquid crystal

One method of driving an LCD is using an EXCLUSIVE-OR gate, as shown in Fig. 3.7.

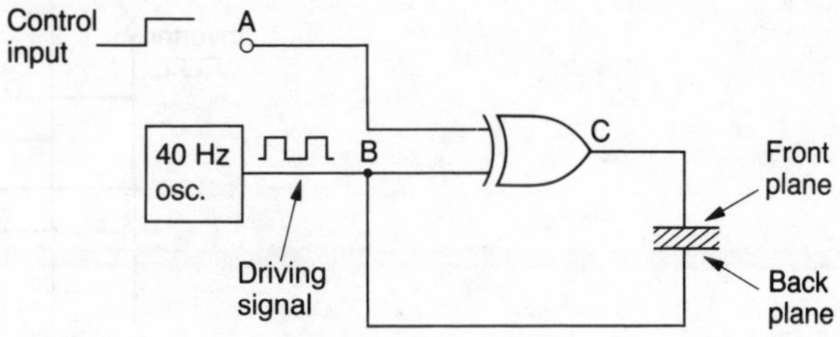

Fig. 3.7 LCD drive

The truth table for an EX-OR gate is as follows:

INPUTS		OUTPUT
A	B	C
0	0	0
1	0	1
0	1	1
1	1	0

From the truth table, it can be seen that when the control input A is low (logical 0), output C follows the input in B, i.e. it is in phase with the 40 Hz driving signal at B. This in-phase signal is fed to the front plane of the LCD segment. At the same time, the back plane is directly fed with the 40 Hz driving signal, resulting in zero electric field across the segment. The segment will be OFF. When control input A is high (logical 1), the output C is out of phase with input B. This out-of-phase driving signal is fed into the front plane of the LCD segment. With the driving signal fed into the back plane, the resultant electric field across the segment has twice the amplitude of the 40 Hz driving signal. The segment will be ON.

Another method of driving the LCD display is to use change-over switches, as shown in Fig. 3.8. The front plane of each segment is driven by its individual switch. When the segment switch is connected to a '0' contact, an in-phase driving signal is fed to the front plane, and the segment is OFF. Conversely, when the segment switch is connected to a '1' contact, an anti-phase driving signal is fed into the front plane and the segment is ON. The segment switches are normally MOS transistors incorporated on the silicon chip itself.

The direct drive techniques described above are only practical for relatively few digits before they become complex and uneconomic. For multi-digit displays, the multiplexing technique described earlier for LED displays is necessary.

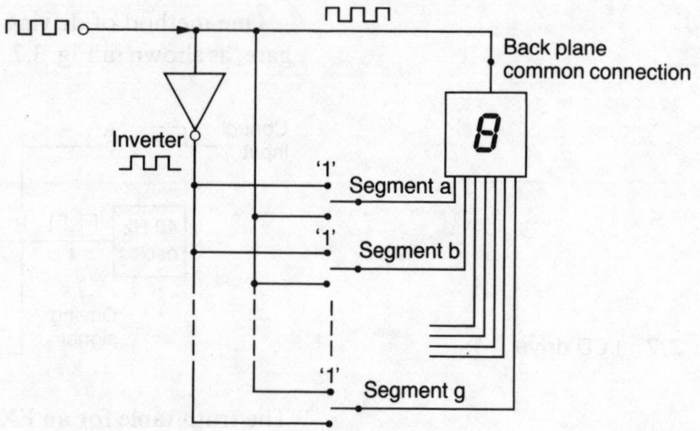

Fig. 3.8 LCD drive

The analogue-to-digital converter, (A/D)

The A/D converter takes the input signal, samples it, and then produces a coded digital signal which corresponds to the level of each sample of the input signal.

There are a number of techniques of analogue-to-digital conversion employed in digital voltmeters. These include:

- single-slope integration,
- dual-slope integration,
- voltage-to-frequency conversion and
- successive approximation.

The most popular type is the dual-slope integration. However, others are also commonly used and warrant explanation.

Converters differ in speed of sampling. The dual-slope takes 2½ readings per second. Faster converters employing the successive approximation method can take up to 200 readings per second. The slower types are used for laboratory equipment, where a visual output is required, while the faster types are employed in systems where a readout is not necessary, the measurement being fed directly into the system for processing.

Single-slope converter

This method converts the voltage level of the input into a measure of time.

The operation of the converter is based on integrating the input voltage to produce a straight ramp voltage. The ramp generator is normally a constant current integrator using an operational amplifier. Figure 3.9(a) shows a simplified block diagram, together with its associated waveforms (Fig. 3.9(b)). The ramp generator produces a linearly increasing voltage with a slope determined by the reference voltage. The analogue input voltage is compared with the instantaneous ramp voltage. While the input voltage is greater than the instantaneous ramp voltage, the output from the comparator is positive, keeping the AND gate open. The pulses produced by the crystal-controlled clock-pulse generator are fed into the decade counter. This continues until the ramp voltage reaches the level of the input voltage. When this happens, the comparator output drops to zero and the gate closes, halting the count. The number of clock pulses counted is thus proportional to the voltage level of the input. A readout of the voltage level may therefore be displayed. The process is continuously repeated for

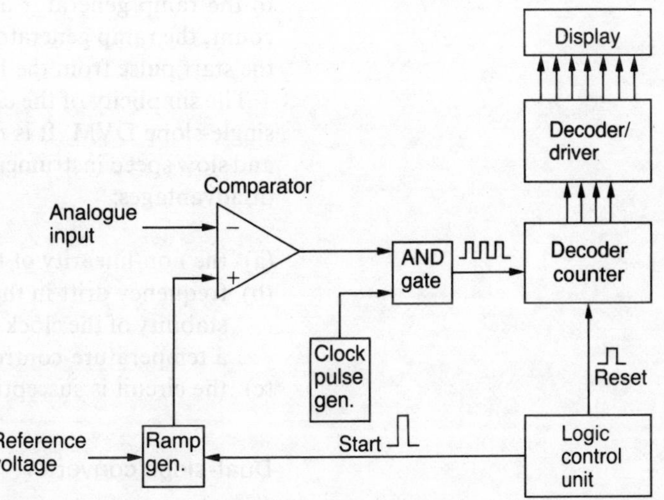

Fig. 3.9 Single-slope converter (a)

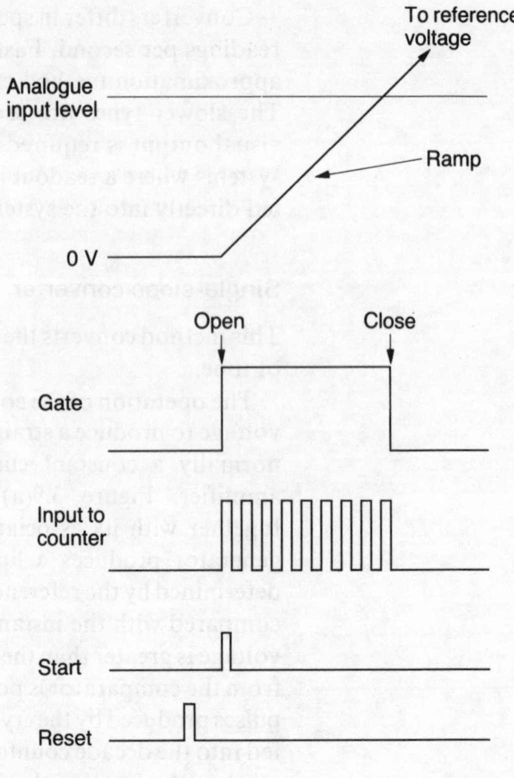

(b)

Fig. 3.9 (Continued)

different samples of the input. The logic control unit commences each sampling operation by sending start and reset trigger pulses to the ramp generator and the counter respectively. After each count, the ramp generator is brought down to zero volt ready for the start pulse from the logic control.

The simplicity of the circuit is the most attractive feature of the single-slope DVM. It is most useful for medium accuracy (0.1%) and slow speed instruments. However, it suffers from a number of disadvantages:

(a) the non-linearity of the ramp voltage,
(b) frequency drift in the clock-pulse generator. To improve the stability of the clock generator, the crystal oscillator is kept in a temperature-controlled oven,
(c) the circuit is susceptible to noise.

Dual-slope converter

The dual-slope converter uses the same basic principle of integration as the single-slope type, but gives superior performance.

In the dual-slope converter, the input voltage is integrated for a specific period of time (t_1 in Fig. 3.10(b)) by charging a capacitor. The capacitor is then discharged at a constant rate towards a reference voltage of the opposite polarity. The time it takes the capacitor to discharge to zero (t_2 in Fig. 3.10(b)) is a measure of the input voltage.

Figure 3.10(a) shows a simplified block diagram for a dual-slope type DVM. The measuring operation starts with S_1 switched to connect the input voltage to the integrator. The output of the integrator is the negative-going ramp shown in Fig. 3.10(b) with a slope of $-\frac{V_{in}}{R_1C_1}$ where R_1C_1 is the time constant of the

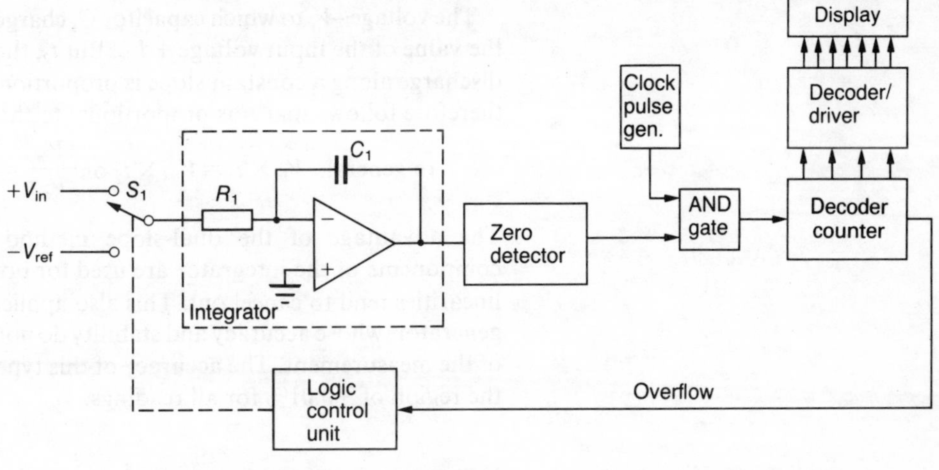

(a)

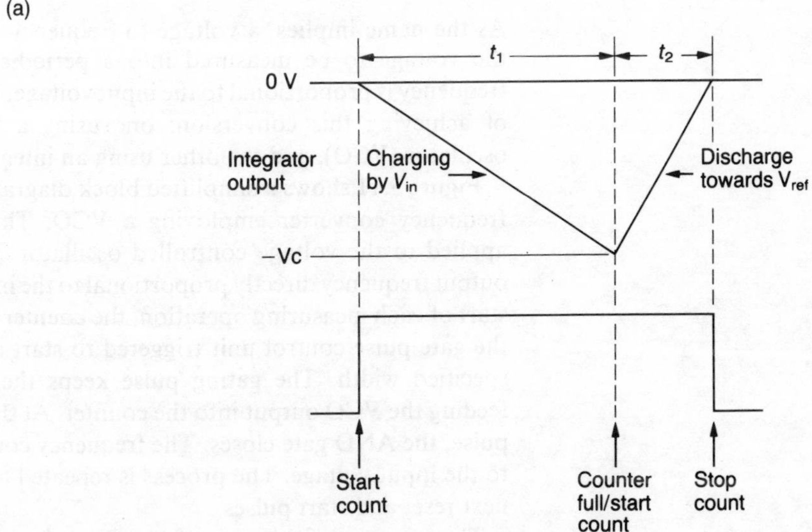

Fig. 3.10 Dual-slope converter (b)

integrator. At the same time as the ramp begins, the AND gate is opened and clock pulses are fed into the counter. This continues until the counter is full (9999 for a four-digit counter). The next clock pulse resets the counter to 0000. When that happens, an overflow trigger pulse is fed to the logic control unit which operates S_1 to disconnect V_{in} from the integrator and connect the reference $-V_{ref}$ in its place. The integrator capacitor C_1 now begins to discharge towards $-V_{ref}$ along the ramp shown in Fig. 3.10(b) with a slope of $\frac{V_{ref}}{R_1C_1}$. When C_1 is discharged back to zero, the zero detector operates, closing the AND gate, halting the count, and displays a reading. The process is then repeated for the next sample.

The voltage $-V_c$ to which capacitor C_1 charges is proportional to the value of the input voltage $+V_{in}$. But t_2, the time it takes C_1 to discharge along a constant slope is proportional to voltage $-V_c$. It therefore follows that t_2 is proportional to the input voltage V_{in}.

In general, $V_{in} \times t_1 = V_{ref} \times t_2$ or $\frac{V_{in}}{V_{ref}} = \frac{t_2}{t_1}$

The advantage of the dual-slope method is that since the components of the integrator are used for both ramps, any non-linearities tend to cancel out. This also applies to the clock-pulse generator, whose accuracy and stability do not affect the accuracy of the measurement. The accuracy of this type of instrument is in the region of ∓0.01% for all readings.

Voltage-to-frequency converter

As the name implies, a voltage-to-frequency converter converts the voltage to be measured into a periodic waveform whose frequency is proportional to the input voltage. There are two ways of achieving this conversion: one using a voltage controlled oscillator (VCO), and the other using an integrator.

Figure 3.11 shows a simplified block diagram for a voltage-to-frequency converter employing a VCO. The input voltage is applied to the voltage controlled oscillator which produces an output frequency directly proportional to the input voltage. At the start of each measuring operation, the counter is reset to zero and the gate pulse control unit triggered to start a gating pulse of a specified width. The gating pulse keeps the AND gate open, feeding the VCO output into the counter. At the end of the gating pulse, the AND gate closes. The frequency count is proportional to the input voltage. The process is repeated at the arrival of the next reset and start pulses.

The accuracy of this type of converter depends on the linearity of the VCO. Higher accuracy may be obtained by using an integrator to produce the voltage-to-frequency conversion.

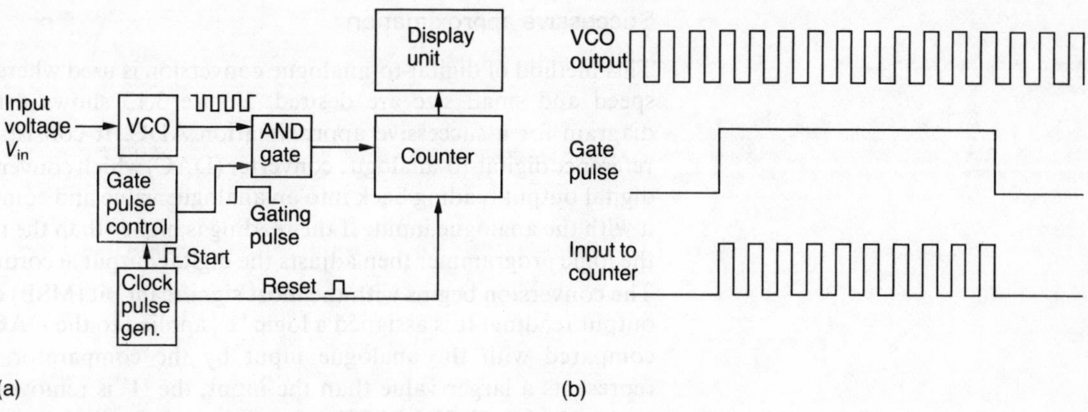

Fig. 3.11 Voltage-to-frequency converter

Figure 3.12(a) shows an integrator type voltage-to-frequency converter with associated waveforms. The input voltage is applied to the integrator which produces the ramp voltage shown. When this ramp voltage reaches the reference voltage, the output of the comparator changes state triggering the pulse generator which in turn causes the integrator to discharge its capacitor. The comparator is then reset and a new ramp starts. The time taken by the integrator capacitor to charge up to the reference voltage V_{ref} is proportional to the input voltage. A high input voltage needs a shorter time than a lower input voltage. This charging time determines the frequency of the output triangular waveform at the integrator and with it the frequency of the comparator output. The output from the comparator is the pulse waveform shown in Fig. 3.12(b). This is fed into the counter to give a measure of the input voltage.

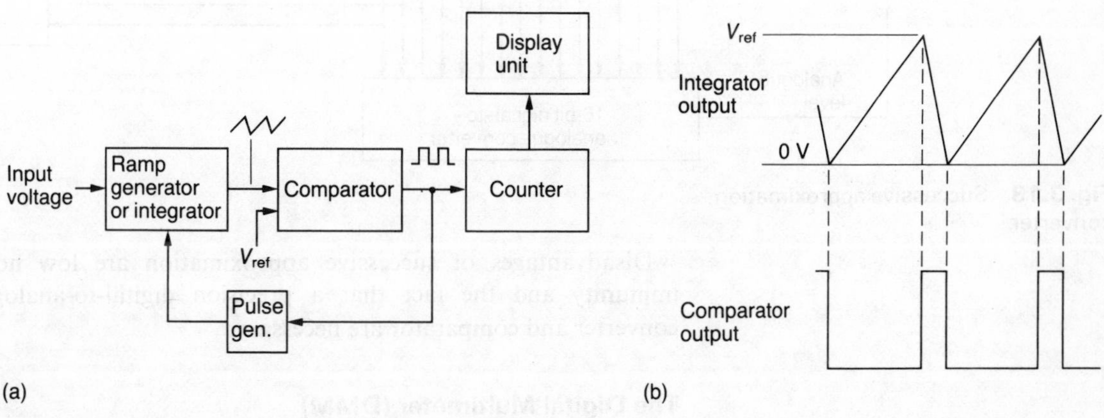

Fig. 3.12 Integrator type voltage-to-frequency converter

Successive approximation

This method of digital-to-analogue conversion is used where high speed and small size are desired. Figure 3.13 shows a block diagram for a successive approximation ADC. It consists of a reference digital-to-analogue converter (DAC) which converts the digital output reading back into an analogue value and compares it with the analogue input. If the reading is higher than the input, the logic programmer then adjusts the digital output accordingly. The conversion begins with the most significant bit (MSB) of the output reading. It is assigned a logic '1', applied to the DAC and compared with the analogue input by the comparator. If it represents a larger value than the input, the '1' is removed and replaced with '0'. If the MSB represents a smaller value than the input, it retains logic '1'. The process is then repeated for the next bit and so on until the voltage output of the DAC is equal to the analogue input to within one half of the least significant bit. This difference is caused by the quantizing error inherent in digital conversion.

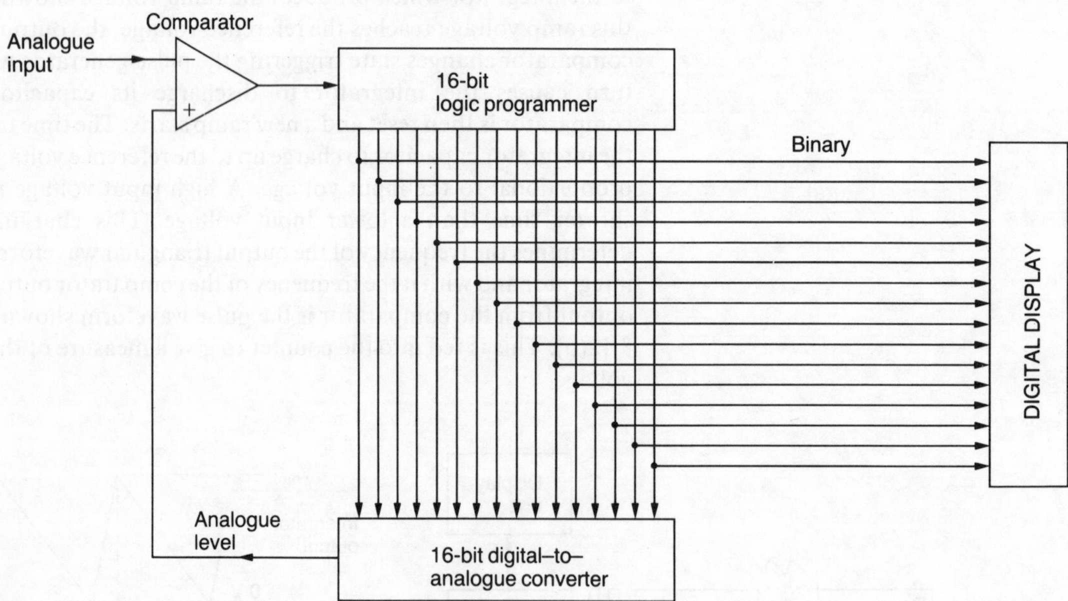

Fig. 3.13 Successive approximation converter

Disadvantages of successive approximation are low noise immunity and the fact that a precision digital-to-analogue converter and comparator are necessary.

The Digital Multimeter (DMM)

Typical digital multimeters measure direct voltage, direct current, resistance, alternating voltage and alternating current. A typical block diagram is shown in Fig. 3.14. The a.c. input is converted to d.c. before going into the analogue-to-digital converter. On the ohms range, another converter is used which drives a current through the resistor under test which is proportional to the value of the resistance. On the ampere range, shunt resistors are connected across the input by closing a switch S_1. Switches S_2 and S_3 are ganged together. A digital output in binary coded decimal is normally provided for direct connection to other digital devices and system applications.

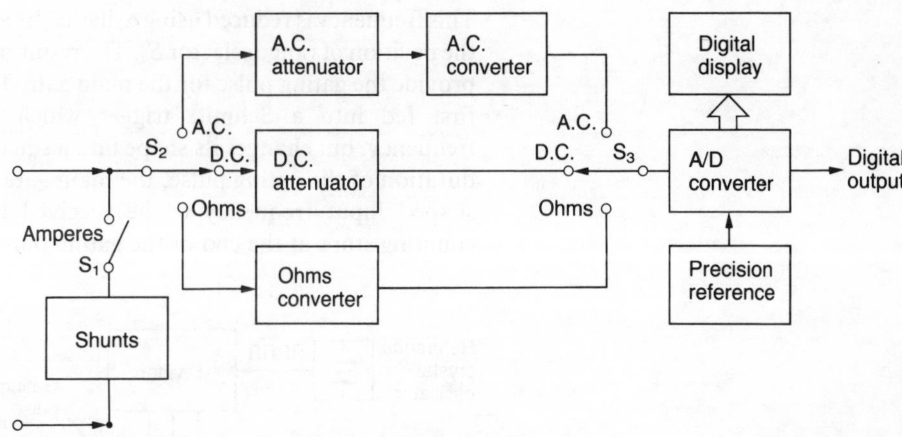

Fig. 3.14 The Digital Multimeter, DMM

The Electronic Counter

The electronic counter is a generic term used to describe digital instruments that make a variety of measurements, such as frequency, period and time interval. The most common are the frequency meter and the timer/counter, which may be used to measure period as well as frequency. Universal counter/timers (UCT) measure time interval as well as frequency and period.

The principle of operation of a counter is shown in Fig. 3.15. It consists of a decade counter with a display preceded by a 2-input AND gate, referred to as the main gate. The AND gate controls the operation of the decade counter. The two inputs to the AND gate A and B may be the start and stop signals to measure a time interval, or a gating pulse and an input signal to measure its frequency or its periodic time.

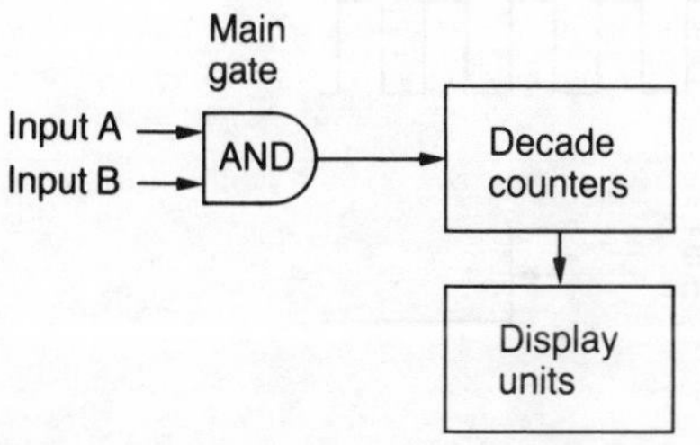

Fig. 3.15 The basic counter

The Frequency Meter

A number of methods may be used to convert a basic counter to measure the frequency of a signal. The main method is the direct gating technique used for measuring low, medium and high frequencies of up to some 700 MHz. For higher frequencies, prescaling or frequency division and other methods must be used. For very low frequencies, right down to fractions of one hertz, reciprocating or low frequency multipliers are used.

Direct gating

Figure 3.16 shows a simplified block diagram for a frequency counter and the associated timing diagram is shown in Fig. 3.17. The crystal oscillator provides a standard reference frequency. This frequency is reduced using a divider by a factor determined by the position of range selector S_1. The resulting waveform is used to provide the gating pulse for the main gate. The input frequency is first fed into a Schmitt trigger which maintains the same frequency, but changes its shape into a square waveform. For the duration of the gating pulse, the main gate is open, allowing the shaped input frequency to be received by the counter. The counting stops at the end of the gating pulse.

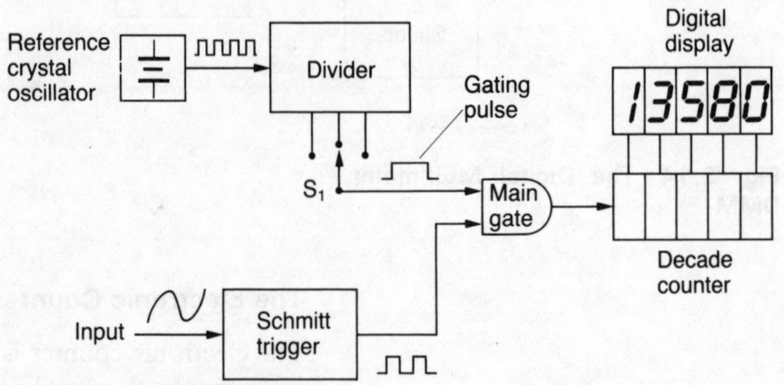

Fig. 3.16 Principles of direct gating

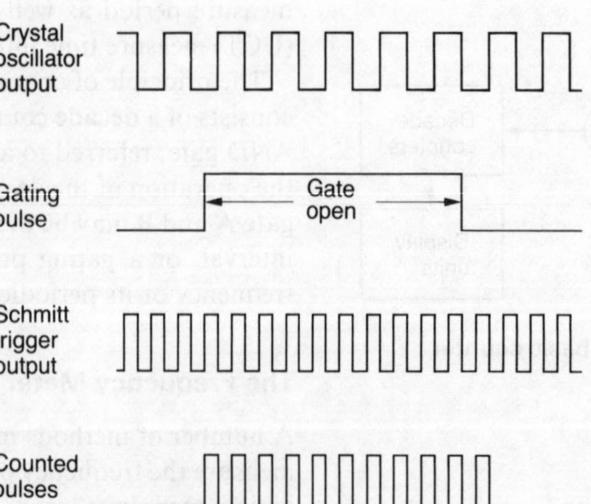

Fig. 3.17 Timing diagram for direct gating counter

Given a gating pulse width (i.e. duration) of 100 ms and an input frequency of 1 kHz, then the number of cycles counted is

$100\ (\text{ms}) \times 1\ (\text{kHz}) = 100 \times 10^{-3} \times 1 \times 10^{3}$
$= 100$ cycles. The digital readout displays 100 representing 1 kHz. It is therefore calibrated to read 1.00 kHz.

In general, if gating time is t and input frequency is f then

$$\text{no. of cycles registered} = t \times f$$

The process described above has to be continuously repeated for successive samples of the input frequency to update the readout. To do this, a logic control unit has to be incorporated as shown in Fig. 3.18. The function of the logic control is to co-ordinate the timing of the various events in the measurement process. At the end of each gating pulse, the main gate closes and the result is displayed. The displayed reading is stored or latched to ensure continuous reading on the display. The stored reading is updated at the end of each count so that the readout only changes when the input frequency changes. At the end of the gating pulse, the logic control unit resets the decade counters to zero, ready for the next sample count. Following a short 'display time' interval, the logic control initiates the start of the next sample by a start command into the divider.

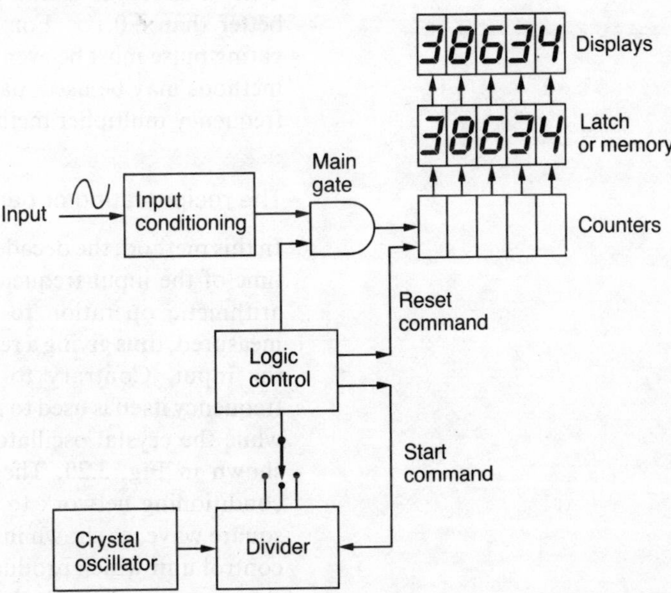

Fig. 3.18 Block diagram for direct gating counter

The Schmitt trigger in Fig. 3.16 has been replaced by the input conditioning unit shown in Fig. 3.18 which contains all other necessary input circuitry to operate the counter. In addition to a

Schmitt trigger it consists of an attenuator, and an amplifier as shown in Fig. 3.19.

Fig. 3.19 Components of input conditioning unit

Low-frequency counters

In the direct gating method, the input frequency is directly gated by the main gate to the decade counters. The duration of the count is determined by the duration of the gating pulse obtained from the reference oscillator. For very low frequencies, the duration of the gating pulse has to be inhibitly long if the accuracy of the instrument is not to suffer. This is because of the inherent ∓1 count error, i.e. the quantizing error described earlier. Assuming a gating pulse of 1 s, a frequency of 1000 Hz will be displayed as 1000 ∓1 representing a possible error of $\mp \frac{1}{1000} \times 100\% = \mp 0.1\%$. A lower frequency, say 10 Hz, will be displayed as 10 ∓1. This represents an error of $\mp \frac{1}{10} \times 100 = \mp 10\%$. To reduce this error to 0.1%, the gating pulse must be lengthened to 100 s. In this case, the display will read $10\text{ Hz} \times 100\text{ s} \mp 1 = 1000 \mp 1$ representing an error of ∓0.1%. A longer gating pulse will be necessary for an accuracy better than ∓0.1%. For lower freqencies, e.g. 1 Hz or less, the gating pulse must be even longer. To overcome this problem, two methods may be used, namely the reciprocating method and the frequency multiplier method.

The reciprocating or period measurement method

In this method, the decade counter is used to measure the periodic time of the input frequency. The instrument then carries out an arithmetic operation to produce the reciprocal of the period measured, thus giving a reading corresponding to the frequency of the input. Contrary to the direct gating method, the input frequency itself is used to provide the gating pulse to the main gate while the crystal oscillator frequency is fed into the counter, as shown in Fig. 3.20. The input frequency is fed into the input conditioning network to convert the signal into an appropriate square wave, as shown in Fig. 3.21. This is then fed into the logic control unit which produces a gating pulse equal to the period of the input signal. While the gating pulse is present at the main gate, the frequency from the reference oscillator, suitably reduced by the divider, is gated into the counters. This is proportional to the period of the input. The arithmetic unit then carries out an inversion operation to obtain the frequency of the input.

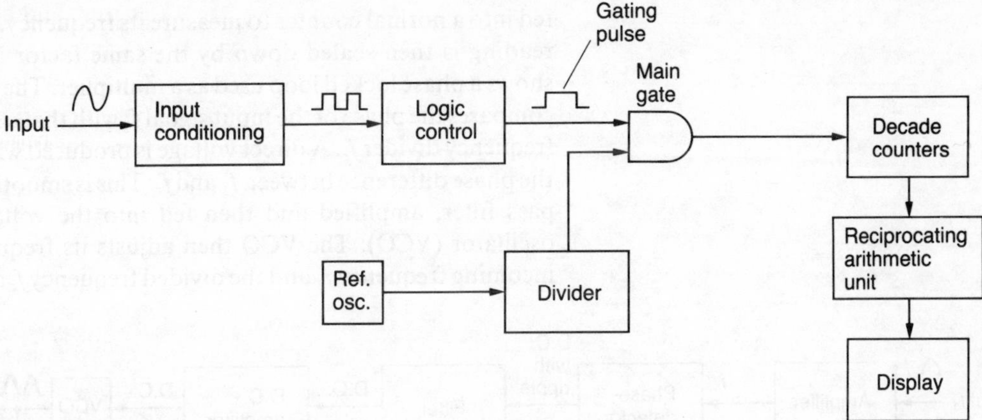

Fig. 3.20 Reciprocating type counter

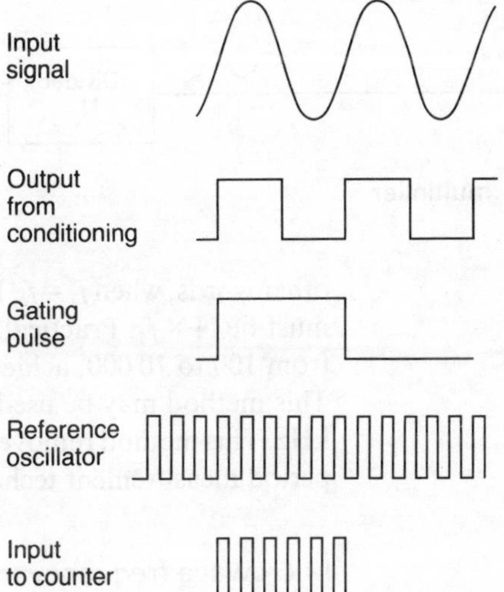

Fig. 3.21 Timing diagram for a reciprocating type

This method produces high accuracy and resolution for frequencies as low as a fraction of 1 Hz. However, it suffers from what is known as triggering error which is caused by noise at the input conditioning unit resulting from the switching process. Such noise can cause the Schmitt trigger to switch over at the wrong time, changing the length of the gating pulse. This is particularly significant for this type of frequency measurement, because the input frequency itself provides the gating pulse and hence the duration of the count.

The frequency multiplier method

This technique employs a phase locked-loop oscillator to multiply the input frequency by a factor N. The multiplied frequency is then fed into a normal counter to measure its frequency. The displayed reading is then scaled down by the same factor N. Figure 3.22 shows a phase locked loop used as a multiplier. The phase detector compares the phase of the input signal f_1 with that coming from the frequency divider f_c. A direct voltage is produced which represents the phase difference between f_1 and f_c. This is smoothed by the low-pass filter, amplified and then fed into the voltage controlled oscillator (VCO). The VCO then adjusts its frequency until the incoming frequency f_1 and the divided frequency f_c are in phase. In

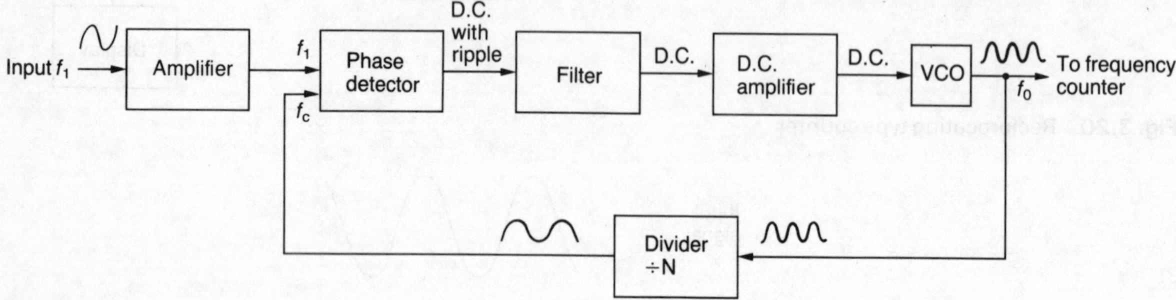

Fig. 3.22 The frequency multiplier type counter

other words, when $f_1 = f_c$. For that to happen the VCO frequency f_0 must be $N \times f_1$. Practical values of N, the multiplier ratio, range from 100 to 10 000, achieving very high accuracy and resolution. This method may be used for frequencies from few Hz to tens of kHz. This method removes the triggering error associated with the period measurement technique.

Microwave frequency meters

As stated earlier, the direct gated method provides frequency measurement up to some 700 MHz. For frequency measurements above 700 MHz (microwave range), other methods must be employed. They involve changing the input frequency to a more convenient value so that it may be measured by a conventional counter. One method is prescaling or dividing the input frequency by a factor of 2 or more using a divider. Another method is the heterodyne technique employing a frequency mixer.

Prescaling or division method

Figure 3.23 shows a block diagram of this type of frequency meter. Following the input conditioning circuitry, the microwave input frequency is reduced by a predetermined factor dependent on the frequency range chosen. The scaled frequency is then gated to the counter in the normal way and a reading is displayed.

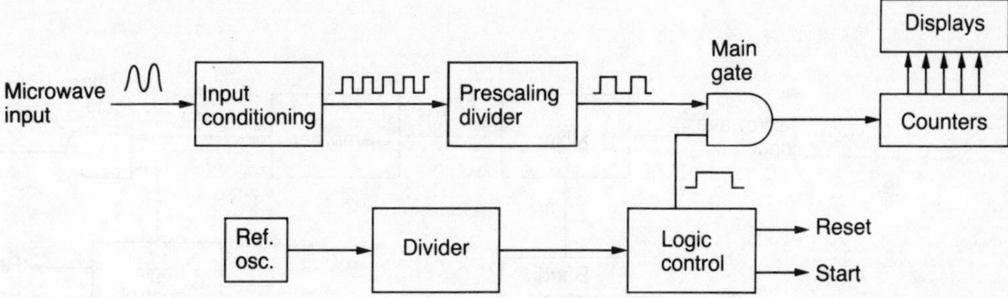

Fig. 3.23 Prescaling or division type counter

With this technique, accuracy and resolution are reduced by a factor equal to the prescaling ratio. For example, given 1 s gating pulse, 1000 Hz input frequency and a prescaling ratio of 1, we get

Count = 1000
displayed reading = 1000 × prescaling factor = 1000 × 1 = 1000
The quantizing error produces a possible error of ∓1
displayed error = ∓1 × prescaling factor = ∓1 × 1 = ∓1.
∴ Resolution = ∓1 Hz

$$\text{And accuracy} = \frac{\mp 1}{1000} \times 100\% = \mp 0.1\%$$

If on the other hand a prescaling ratio of 2 is used then:

$$\text{Count} = \frac{1000}{2} = 500$$

displayed reading = 500 × prescaling factor = 500 × 2 = 1000
Possible error of ∓1
displayed error = ∓1 × prescaling factor = ∓1 × 2 = ∓2.
∴ Resolution = ∓2 Hz

$$\text{And accuracy} = \frac{\mp 2}{1000} \times 100\% = \mp 0.2\%$$

For this reason, the prescaling factor is limited to approximately 3 giving a maximum frequency of 2000 MHz.

The heterodyne converter

For frequencies above 2000 MHz, the heterodyne method may be used. Figure 3.24 shows a manually tuned heterodyne frequency meter. The input frequency f_1 is mixed with a local frequency f_{oh} derived from a tuned band-pass filter. The mixer produces a difference frequency $f_1 - f_{oh}$ within the range of a conventional frequency counter. The reference crystal oscillator is used to provide the mixer with local frequency f_{oh}. The output from the

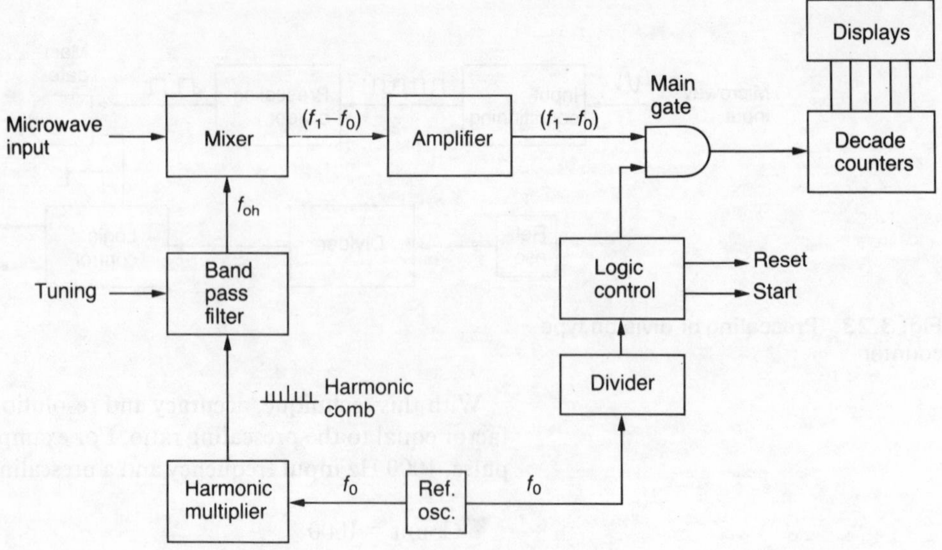

Fig. 3.24 The heterodyne frequency counter

reference oscillator is fed into a harmonic multiplier which provides a 'comb' output with harmonic frequencies known as the 'teeth' spaced at regular intervals. The tuned filter then selects one of these harmonics to feed into the mixer. The selection of the harmonic is carried out manually by tuning the filter upwards towards the input frequency. The frequency of the input is then obtained by adding the readout to the selected frequency of the filter.

Modern counters of this type use microprocessor control for automatic heterodyne conversion. The processor controls the filter and determines the local frequency f_{oh}. This frequency is fed into the mixer to produce the frequency difference $f_1 - f_{oh}$ as explained earlier.

The processor stores the value of the local frequency f_{oh} and uses it to calculate the input frequency once the difference frequency $f_1 - f_{oh}$ has been measured by the conventional counter. Apart from controlling the filter and calculating the input frequency, the processor resets the decade counters, sends the start command to the divider, and selects its division factor.

Other Measurements Using Counters

Periodic time

The technique used for the reciprocating method of measuring low frequencies may be used to measure the period of an input signal. As explained earlier in this chapter, the input signal is used as the gating pulse. The main gate is kept open for the duration of the period of the input signal, while the counter counts the number of cycles from the reference oscillator which gives a measure of the period of the input signal.

Time interval

Figure 3.25 shows a block diagram for measuring the time interval between two events. The start signal is used to open the main gate and begin the count. The stop signal closes the gate and the count ceases. The two input signals go through a Schmitt trigger to give the signals the necessary sharp edges to open and close the gate. The Schmitt trigger threshold points become very important in this application. This is because the two signals may be different in amplitude, shape and rise time. For high accuracy of time interval measurements, elaborate methods for input conditioning and trigger calibration and control must be employed.

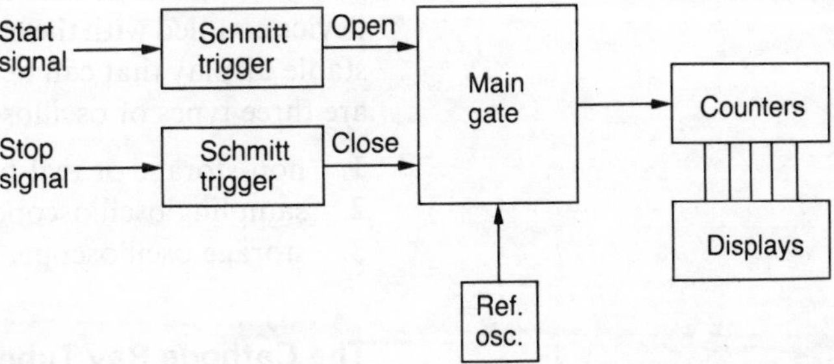

Fig. 3.25 Time interval measurement

Errors in Electronic Counters

1. **Timebase error**. Errors in the reference oscillator produce equal errors in the final readout. These are known as timebase errors.
2. The **quantizing error** of ∓1 digit.
3. **Trigger error**. This is caused by noise affecting the triggering of the Schmitt trigger. It is especially important in period measurement technique.

4 Cathode ray oscilloscope

The Cathode Ray Oscilloscope (CRO) is one of the most versatile test instruments which, apart from displaying wave shape, may be used to measure voltage level, period and hence frequency, and phase relationship with other waveforms. It can also measure distortion, noise, modulation depth, rise time of pulse waveforms and the bandwidth of an amplifier.

The oscilloscope uses a cathode ray tube (CRT) as the display device coupled with the necessary circuitry to ensure a continuous stable display that can be used for measurement purposes. There are three types of oscilloscopes:

1. non-storage or real-time oscilloscope,
2. sampling oscilloscope,
3. storage oscilloscope.

The Cathode Ray Tube

The principle of operation of the CRT is that a negative hot cathode emits electrons which, when collected by an anode held at a positive potential relative to the cathode, results in an electric current being established in the form of an electron beam. This is known as thermionic emission.

Figure 4.1 is a diagrammatical sketch showing the construction of a CRT. The electron gun is the cathode emitting the electrons

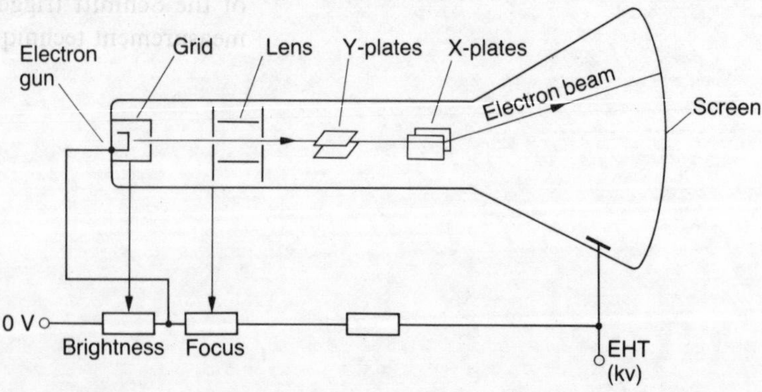

Fig. 4.1 The Cathode Ray Tube

which go through an aperture in the grid. The grid, which is made more negative than the cathode, controls the number of electrons emitted by the gun, and hence the brightness of the display. The electron beam goes through an electrostatic lens to focus the beam on the screen. The screen is coated on the inside with a fluorescent powder (e.g. phosphor) which gives a visible glow when struck by the high-speed electrons. The electron beam generated by the electron gun and focused by the lens, produces a stationary spot on the screen. To produce a trace, the beam must be deflected in both the horizontal and vertical directions. Electrostatic deflection is employed, where pairs of plates are used to deflect the beam: two X-plates for horizontal deflection and two Y-plates for the vertical deflection. The beam passes between the two pairs of deflecting plates, the potential differences on the plates determining the deflection angle.

The Oscilloscope

Real-time display

Figure 4.2 shows a basic block diagram for a real-time single display oscilloscope. The input is first fed into an attenuator which provides the necessary signal conditioning for the main vertical amplifier. The vertical amplifier is a wide-band amplifier feeding the Y-plates of the CRT to provide the vertical deflection. The vertical displacement of the spot on the screen at any instant is determined by the Y input voltage at the same instant. This is known as real-time display in which the Y-input voltage is immediately displayed on the screen as a vertical deflection. However, with no corresponding horizontal movement, a vertical straight line will be displayed on the screen.

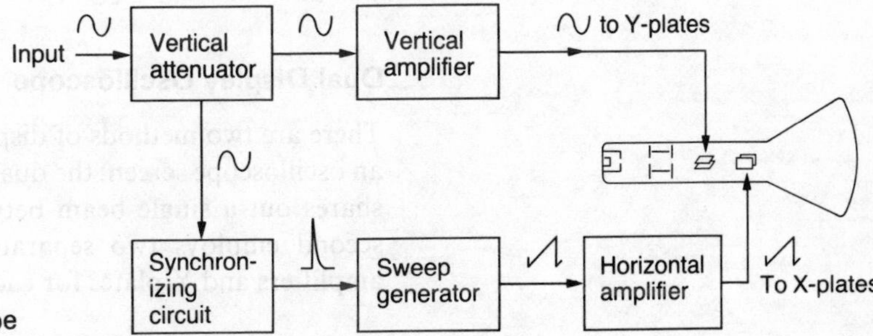

Fig. 4.2 Single display oscilloscope

To provide the horizontal movement, the X-plates are fed with a saw-tooth waveform known as the timebase, shown in Fig. 4.3. This timebase, produced by the sweep generator, moves the electron beam at a uniform speed across the screen from left to right (the sweep). At the end of the sweep, the beam is rapidly returned back to its starting point on the left-hand side of the

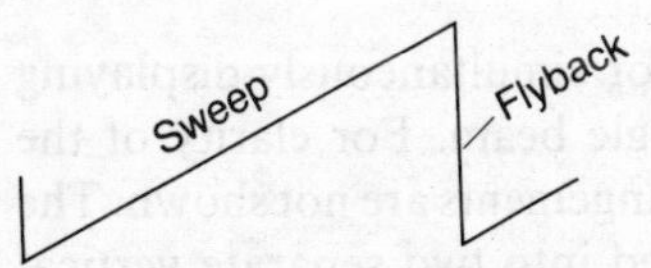

Fig. 4.3 Timebase waveform

screen (the flyback). The simultaneous movement of the beam in the vertical and horizontal directions produces a trace of the input waveform. For a steady observable trace, the same portion of the input signal must be traced repeatedly by the timebase. It is necessary, therefore, to synchronize the horizontal movement with the input signal. That is to say, each horizontal sweep of the screen must commence at an identical point on the input waveform. This is the function of the synchronizing circuitry. Samples of the input signal are employed to produce pulses which are used to trigger the sweep generator which locks the display to the frequency speed of the input signal. At low input frequencies, the timebase is correspondingly slow introducing flicker in the displayed waveform. This is an inherent problem associated with real-time oscilloscopes. The CRT screen is provided with a measuring graticule with eight vertical and ten horizontal divisions. The setting of the vertical attenuator provides the voltage calibration, while the setting of the speed (or frequency) of the sweep generator provides time calibration.

Delay

As can be seen from the block diagram in Fig. 4.2, the path of the synchronizing signal, and hence the commencement of the X-sweep, is longer than the path for the Y-deflecting signal. A time delay therefore exists between the arrival of the Y-signal and the start of the X-deflection. The result is that the oscilloscope is unable to display the leading part of the input cycle. This becomes very important in pulse application where the leading edge is of vital significance. To overcome this, a time delay is introduced in the Y-signal path as it leaves the vertical amplifier. Enough delay is introduced to allow the portion of the input signal which initiates the synchronizing trigger, to be displayed on the screen.

Dual Display Oscilloscope

There are two methods of displaying two simultaneous traces on an oscilloscope screen: the dual trace and the dual beam. The first shares out a single beam between two input signals, while the second employs two separate beams with independent guns, amplifiers and Y-plates for each input signal.

Dual trace

Figure 4.4 shows an arrangement for simultaneously displaying two input signals, employing a single beam. For clarity of the essential operation the timebase arrangements are not shown. The two input signals Y1 and Y2 are fed into two separate vertical pre-amplifiers. The main function of the pre-amplifiers is to

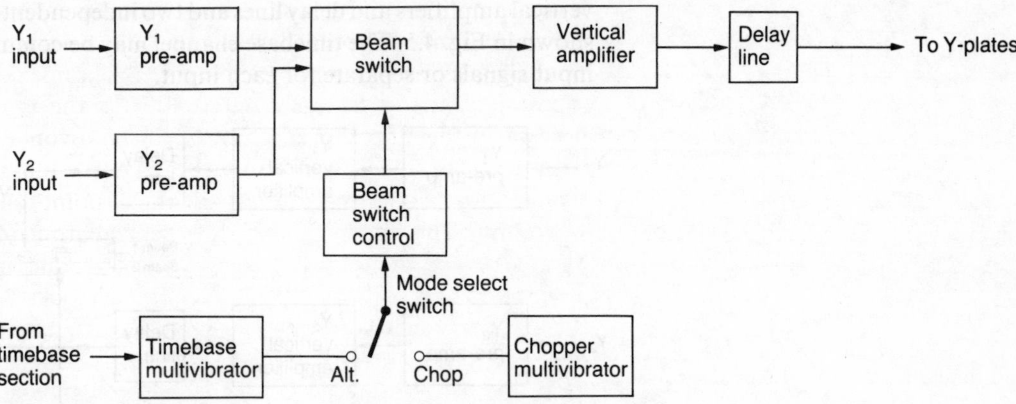

Fig. 4.4 Dual trace oscilloscope

provide the necessary signal conditioning in terms of attenuation or amplification and input impedance. The pre-amplifiers must provide an adequate range of gain or attenuation so as to allow input signals with a wide variety of amplitudes to be displayed by the oscilloscope. The outputs from the two pre-amplifiers are connected to the vertical amplifier in sequence: Y1, Y2, Y1 and so on. Switching between the two channels is carried out by the beam switch with the switching speed determined by the beam switch control. The single electron beam is thus shared between the two inputs.

Time-sharing of the electron beam may be carried out in two ways:

(i) The alternate mode where the switching between the two channels takes place once every sweep. The timebase sweep alternates between Y1 and Y2. This mode is appropriate for high sweep speeds (i.e. high input frequencies). However, at slow speeds of the sweep generator, the switching between the two channels becomes visible and flicker occurs. To overcome this, the second method is used.

(ii) The chopped mode which uses a fast rate of switching between the two channels. The chopper multivibrator provides a high switching frequency resulting in the beam switch operating more than once during a single sweep.

The mode select switch may be operated manually or may be linked to the timebase control.

Before the switched signal is applied to the Y-plates, a delay line is introduced, as shown, to ensure the display of the leading part of the input signals.

Dual beam

The dual-beam oscilloscope employs two completely independent vertical channels: two independent electron guns, two independent vertical amplifiers and delay lines and two independent Y-plates as shown in Fig. 4.5. The timebase channel may be common to both input signals or separate for each input.

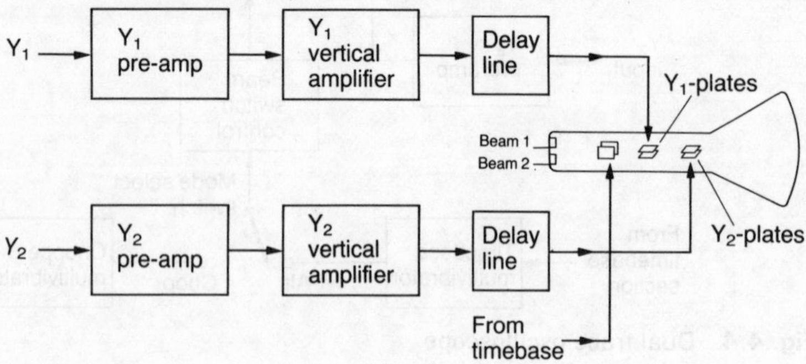

Fig. 4.5 Dual beam oscilloscope

Advantages and disadvantages

While the dual-trace oscilloscope is cheaper, it suffers from its inability to switch between the two channels at a very fast rate. It is therefore unsuitable for simultaneous measurement of two fast transient events. For such applications, the dual beam must be used.

Delayed Sweep

Normal sweep operations are unsuitable for the detailed observation and measurement of specific portions of a display, e.g. the leading edge of a pulse, ringing, etc. Delayed sweeps add a specific amount of time between the trigger pulse and the beginning of the sweep. The start of the sweep may thus be controlled allowing a small segment of the waveform to be enlarged and observed for accurate measurements to be carried out.

Probes

A requirement of an oscilloscope, like other measuring instruments, is that it should produce the input signals faithfully without distortion. In high frequency and pulse applications, the input capacitance of the oscilloscope begins to load the circuit under measurement reducing the high frequency response. To overcome this, probes are used. The effect of the probe is to increase the input resistance of the oscilloscope while lowering its input capacitance. Figure 4.6 shows the use of a probe in conjunction with a coaxial cable lead. The cable represents a capacitive load C_c shunting the signal to be measured. The probe consists of a capacitor C_p shunting a series resistor R_p. Probe capacitor C_p is in series with the effective input capacitance of the oscilloscope (C_i shunted by C_c)

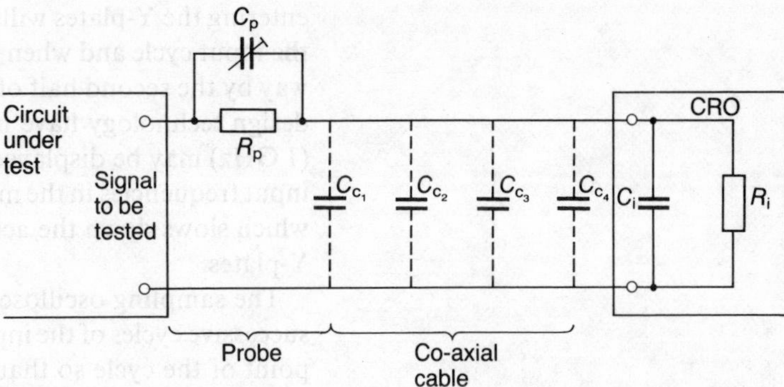

Fig. 4.6 The passive probe

reducing the total capacitance presented to the signal to be measured. The probe resistor R_p, while raising the resistance presented to the signal to be measured, reduces the signal level to the oscilloscope input terminals.

A common probe is the 10:1 attenuator or divider probe. Using this probe, all voltage reading on the oscilloscope must be multiplied by a factor of 10 to give the actual level of the measured signal. A typical 10:1 probe (C_p = 12 pF, R_p = 9 MΩ with an oscilloscope input resistance of 1 MΩ) will present an input resistance of 10 MΩ and an input capacitance of 8 pF. The same probe may be used with other instruments such as an EVM to reduce their loading effect.

The input capacitance of an oscilloscope varies with the setting of the Y attenuator. For this reason C_p is made variable as shown in Fig. 4.6. C_p is adjusted to ensure best results by observing a square wave on the screen. Many oscilloscopes provide a 1 MHz square wave output precisely for this purpose. Figure 4.7 shows the three possible waveform reproductions on the oscilloscope screen. Correct setting of C_p gives the square wave shown in (a). Under compensation results in rounded edges (b) while over-compensation produces overshoots (c).

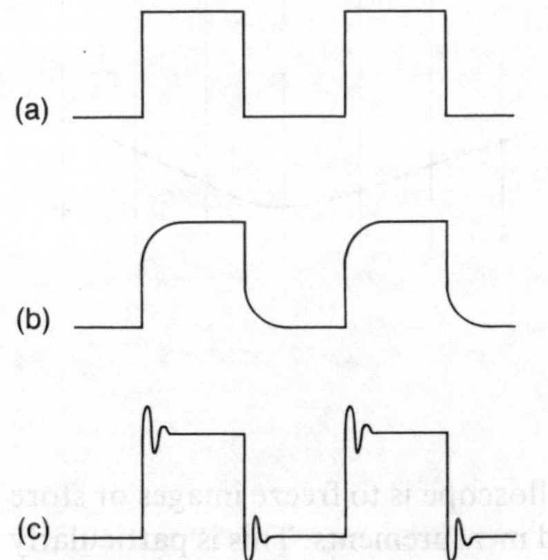

Fig. 4.7 Effect of varying probe capacitor C_p

The reduced capacitive loading of an oscilloscope obtained by the use of the *passive probe* described above is achieved at the price of reduced sensitivity, usually by a factor of 10. To overcome this, probes may be provided with a high impedance buffer amplifier to compensate for the loss in sensitivity. Such probes are known as *active probes.*

Sampling Oscilloscopes

The real-time display oscilloscope described above, can display signals of 100 MHz or even higher. The transit time, i.e. the time the electron takes to travel through the Y deflection plates, puts a limit to the frequency that the oscilloscope can handle. This limit is reached when the period of the input signal approaches the transit time between the Y-plates. At such a situation, the electron beam entering the Y-plates will be deflected one way by the first half of the input cycle and when halfway down the Y-plates the opposite way by the second half of the input cycle. Improvements in CRT design technology have meant that frequencies up to 1000 MHz (1 GHz) may be displayed by real-time oscilloscopes. For higher input frequencies in the microwave region, sampling must be used which slows down the actual deflecting frequency applied to the Y-plates.

The sampling oscilloscope takes a sample of the amplitude of successive cycles of the input signal. Each sample is taken at a later point of the cycle so that a complete picture of the waveform is constructed, as shown in Fig. 4.8.

Sampling oscilloscopes have high sensitivity and can provide very clear displays of microwave signals (GHz). However, the input signal must be repetitive. Single shot events or narrow transients cannot be captured by this method. To observe such waveforms, storage oscilloscopes have to be used.

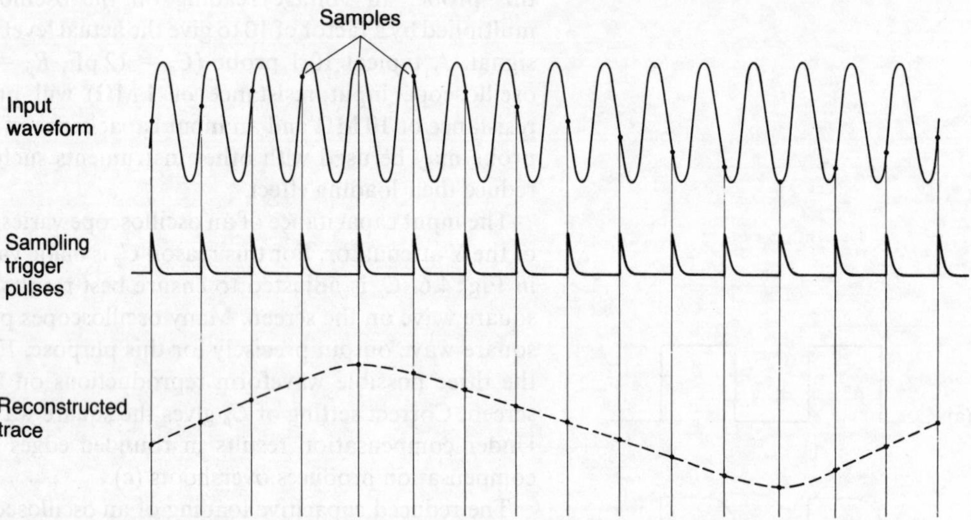

Fig. 4.8 Construction of a waveform display by sampling

Storage Oscilloscopes

The purpose of a storage oscilloscope is to freeze images or store them for later observation and measurements. This is particularly useful for single-shot events such as transients and glitches (unwanted spikes on pulse waveforms) and for displaying low-frequency waveforms without the flicker associated with real-time oscilloscopes.

There are two types of storage oscilloscopes:

1. the analogue type which uses a storage cathode ray tube;
2. the digitizing storage type.

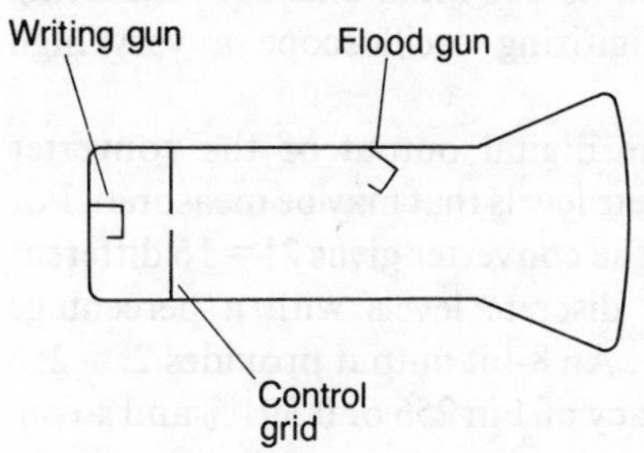

Fig. 4.9 Analogue storage oscilloscope

The analogue storage oscilloscope

In this type of storage oscilloscope, the complete waveform is captured and stored by the tube itself. The storage tube employs two guns: the conventional electron gun known as the 'writing gun' and a second gun known as the 'floodgun', see Fig. 4.9. The analogue storage oscilloscope stores the trace's image on the screen surface for examination later in its original form. It involves no sampling and the whole waveform is displayed, this being the principal advantage of the analogue type over the digitizing type. However, the analogue type cannot manipulate the trace once it has been captured by the tube, e.g. expanding parts of the trace for detailed examination. Another disadvantage of analogue storage is its high cost when compared with the digitizing type.

The digitizing storage oscilloscope

There is little doubt that as in all aspects of electronics, digital technology is the major trend in the design and manufacture of oscilloscopes. As analogue-to-digital (A-to-D) converters improve in performance, so will the digitizing oscilloscope become the dominant type in the market.

The basic structure of the digitizing oscilloscope is that the input signal is converted into a digital form and stored in memory. It is then converted back into an analogue signal, reconstructed and presented on the CRT screen for permanent display, see Fig. 4.10. This allows the image of unrepetitive single-shot (rare event) to be presented with the brightness of a continuous signal using a low-cost conventional tube. The image, once stored in memory, can stay there permanently, and it may be expanded or compared with previously captured waveform. Further, the waveform being in digital form may be used directly to interact with other digital devices, e.g. feeding into a computer for processing. The fact that the digitizing storage oscilloscope employs an A-to-D converter means that some form of sampling is involved. The converter, also known as the digitizer, looks at the level of samples of the input signal and produces a digital code which represents the voltage level of each sample. The accuracy or resolution of the oscilloscope ultimately depends on the sampling rate as well as the number of binary bits at the output of the converter.

The speed of sampling is controlled by a local clock oscillator

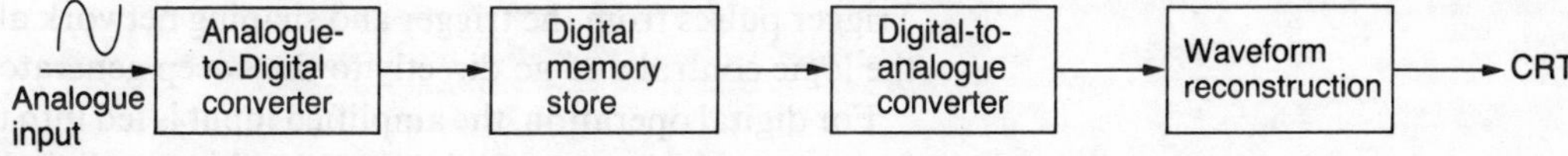

Fig. 4.10 Basic structure of a digitizing oscilloscope

which triggers the A-to-D converter. Sampling rates of 1 or 2 MHz are normal. Higher rates such as 100 MHz and over are being produced, which give the digitizing oscilloscope a very high accuracy.

The number of bits of the digital output of the converter determine the number of discrete levels that may be measured. For example, a 4-bit output from the converter gives $2^4 = 16$ different binary combinations, i.e. 16 discrete levels with a percentage resolution of 1 in 16 or 6.25%. An 8-bit output provides $2^8 = 256$ discrete levels giving an accuracy of 1 in 256 or 0.391% and so on.

The sampling involved in the digitizing type oscilloscope is not the same as that used in the sampling oscilloscopes. While the sampling oscilloscope takes one sample of successive cycles, the digitizing oscilloscope takes several samples of one cycle, as shown in Fig. 4.11.

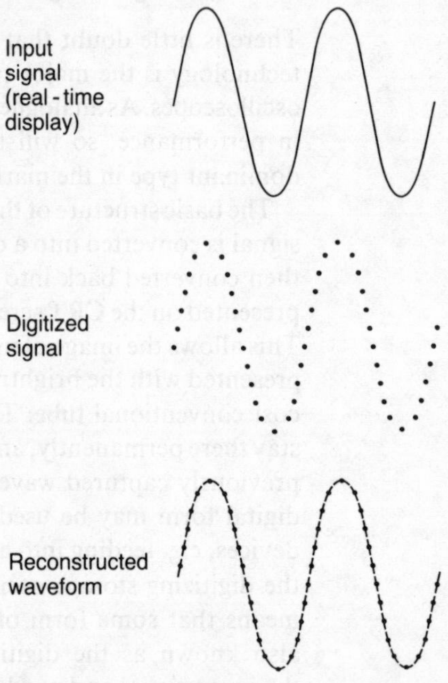

Fig. 4.11

Figure 4.12 shows a block diagram for a single channel digitizing storage oscilloscope. Facility is provided for the oscilloscope to function as a conventional real-time oscilloscope. By operating linked switches S1/S2, the digitizing section may be bypassed feeding the amplified input signal directly into the tube. Trigger pulses from the trigger and shaping network also by-pass the logic control and go directly to the sweep generator.

For digital operation, the amplified input is fed into the A-to-D converter, which converts the input level into a digital code. The digital output from the converter is then fed into memory for storage. To reproduce the waveform on the screen, the information

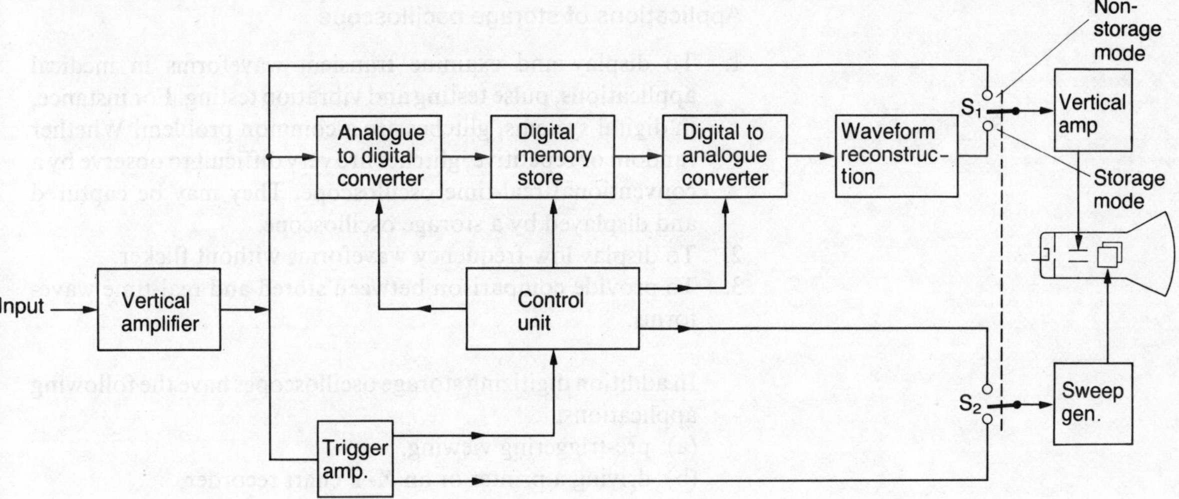

Fig. 4.12 Single channel digitizing storage oscilloscope

stored in memory is first passed through a D-to-A converter, and then reconstructed by joining the dots defined by the D-to-A converter to produce a continuous display.

The logic control ensures the synchronous operation of the oscilloscope. Its functions include:

1. receiving trigger pulses from the trigger and shaping network;
2. determining the sampling rate of the A-to-D converter;
3. controlling the entry of data into the store;
4. controlling the release of the stored data into the D-to-A converter;
5. controlling the D-to-A converter by determining its speed and the release of data of the cathode ray tube.

The control unit starts the storage operation upon the receipt of a trigger pulse from the trigger amplifier. The trigger pulse may be produced externally by closing a switch or internally by a predetermined combination of polarity, slope or level of the input signal. The control unit also receives such information as the timebase setting, which it uses to determine the sampling rate of the A-to-D converter. It then opens the memory to store the digital data produced by the converter. It retains this information until it is required for observation. The control unit will then release the stored data into the D-to-A converter. The control unit may be armed to capture and hold the first occurrence of the trigger conditions, or to continually update the stored and displayed signals as the trigger condition recurs. Pre-triggering may also be used providing the capability of 'looking backwards', i.e. to display the part of the signal prior to the trigger condition.

Applications of storage oscilloscope

1. To display and examine transient waveforms in medical applications, pulse testing and vibration testing. For instance, in digital systems, glitches are a common problem. Whether random or repetitive, glitches are very difficult to observe by a conventional real-time oscilloscope. They may be captured and displayed by a storage oscilloscope.
2. To display low-frequency waveforms without flicker.
3. To provide comparison between stored and real-time waveforms.

In addition digitizing storage oscilloscopes have the following applications:

(a) pre-triggering viewing,
(b) driving a printer or an X-Y chart recorder,
(c) expand small parts of the displayed signal for detailed examination,
(d) unlimited storage, either within the oscilloscope or into an external memory or a computer for analysis.

Measurements Using the Oscilloscope

The oscilloscope may be used for a variety of measurements of the displayed waveform. Up to very recently, these measurements had to be carried out manually. However, modern oscilloscopes provide modular attachments for a DVM for measuring a voltage, counting a frequency, timing a period, pulse width or time interval, and measuring phase difference.

Voltage measurement

The screen of the CRT is provided with a measuring graticule with vertical and horizontal divisions. These divisions, which are normally centimetre divisions, are calibrated for voltage measurements (vertical divisions) and time measurements (horizontal divisions). The graticule is used for almost all the measurements that are carried out by the oscilloscope.

The basic voltage measurement is the peak-to-peak value of the displayed waveform. The number of divisions between the negative and positive peaks correspond to the peak-to-peak voltage. The volt/cm setting provides the scale, e.g. 1 V/cm, 10 mV/cm etc. In Fig. 4.13, for instance, $V_{pp} = 6\text{ cm} \times 2\text{ V/cm} = 12\text{ V}$.

The amplitude, $V_p = \frac{1}{2} V_{pp} = \frac{1}{2} \times 12 = 6\text{ V}$

The r.m.s. value, $V_{rms} = 0.707 \times V_p = 0.707 \times 6 = 4.24\text{ V}$

Measurement of period and frequency

The number of horizontal divisions for one complete cycle of the display represents the period of the waveform. Given the timebase setting, e.g. 1 ms/cm or 10 μs/cm, the period may be calculated. For the waveform shown in Fig. 4.13:

period, $t = 4 \text{ cm} \times 5 \text{ ms/cm} = 20 \text{ ms}$

The frequency f of the waveform may be calculated from

$$f = \frac{1}{t} = \frac{1}{20 \text{ ms}}$$

$$f = 0.05 \text{ kHz} = 50 \text{ Hz}$$

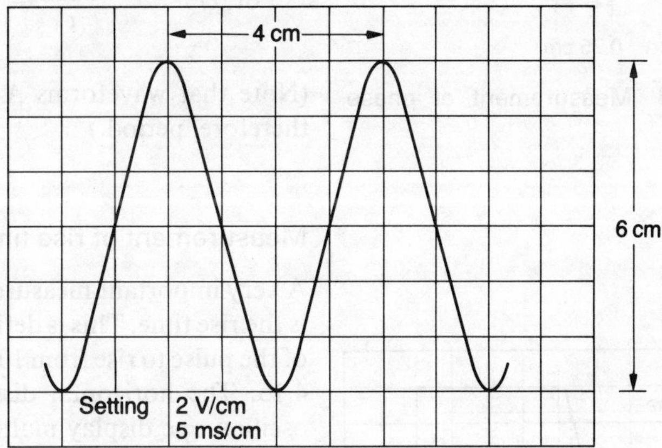

Fig. 4.13 Measurement of voltage and period

This method of determining the frequency may be used for any wave shape. A more accurate method for measuring frequency is to use *Lissajous' figures.* However, this method may be applied to pure waveforms with no harmonics i.e. sinusoidal waveforms only. It relies on comparing an unknown frequency with a known frequency. The accuracy of the measurement thus depends on the accuracy of the known frequency.

Lissajous' figures are produced by switching the internal timebase off and using a known frequency as an external timebase. The ratio between the two frequencies is determined by the number of peaks appearing on a steady Lissajous' figure.

Phase difference measurement

The phase difference between two waveforms is a time difference between the waveforms. An example of two such waveforms is shown in Fig. 4.14 where waveform A leads waveform B by angle ϕ. The graticule is used to measure the distance between any two equivalent points on the two waveforms, e.g. between the two peaks. By using the timebase scale setting, the time interval between the two waveforms may be found. The phase difference itself can then be calculated, as follows.

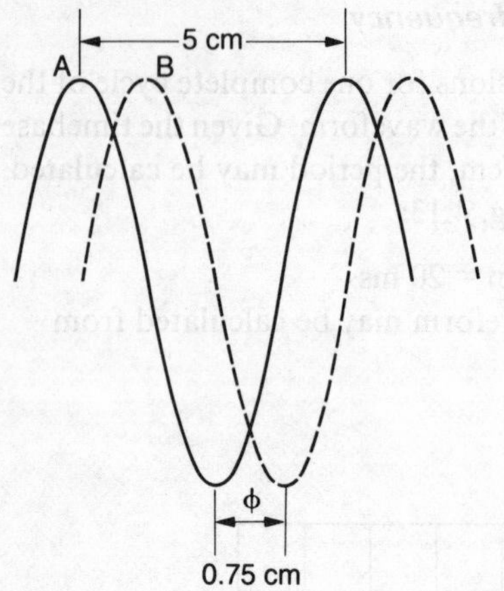

Fig. 4.14 Measurement of phase difference

Given a timebase setting of 2 ms/cm for the display shown in Fig. 4.14, then since the distance between A and B is 0.75 cm, time interval, $T_i = 0.75 \text{ cm} \times 2 \text{ ms/cm} = 1.5 \text{ ms}$.
Period of waveforms $t = 5 \text{ cm} \times 2 \text{ ms/cm} = 10 \text{ ms}$

But period t is equivalent to a phasor angular rotation of 360° or 2π radians.

$$\text{Thus, phase angle, } \phi = \frac{360\, T_i}{t} = \frac{360 \times 1.5}{10} = 54°$$

$$\text{or, } \phi \quad \frac{2\pi\, T_i}{t} = \frac{2\pi \times 1.5}{10} = 0.94 \text{ rad}$$

(Note that waveforms A and B have the same frequency and, therefore, period.)

Measurement of rise time

A very important measurement associated with pulse application is the rise time. This is defined as the time it takes the leading edge of the pulse to rise from 10% to 90% of its final amplitude, see Fig. 4.15. The horizontal distance between the two points on the oscilloscope display multiplied by the timebase setting gives the rise time.

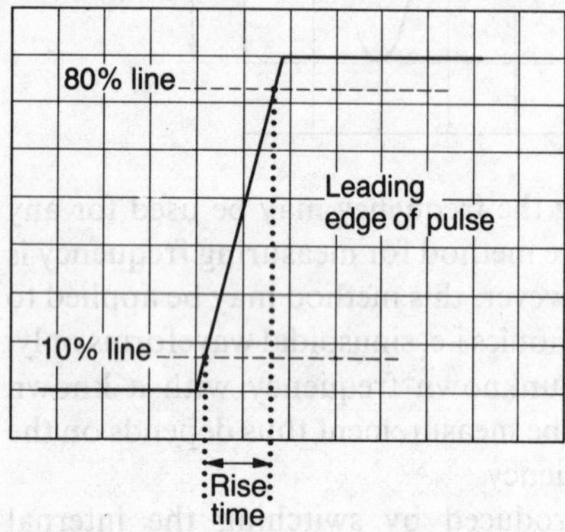

Fig. 4.15 Measurement of rise time

For accurate measurement it is necessary to use an oscilloscope that (a) can trigger and enlarge the leading edge of the pulse, and (b) has an oscilloscope rise time at least five times better (i.e. smaller) than the pulse rise time it intends to display.

The rise time of an oscilloscope is the time the trace takes to rise from 10% to 90% of its final position when the Y input is fed with a perfect, i.e. infinitely rising, step voltage.

The rise time of the oscilloscope is closely linked to its bandwidth. In general, for a conventional real-time oscilloscope, the bandwidth × rise time = 0.35. Thus for a bandwidth of 3 MHz, the oscilloscope has a rise time of

$$\frac{0.35}{3 \times 10^6} = 0.117 \times 10^{-6} = 0.117\ \mu\text{S} = 117 \text{ ns}$$

Such an oscilloscope will be suitable for measuring a pulse rise time in excess of $5 \times 0.117 = 0.585\ \mu$s or 585 ns. An oscilloscope with a rise time comparable to that of the pulse gives a higher value of rise time measurement than the actual value of rise time of the pulse. This is because of the delay caused by the oscilloscope itself. In such cases, the rise time of the pulse, T_p, may be estimated using the following formula:

$$T_p = \sqrt{(T_{m^2} - T_{s^2})}$$

where T_m = measured rise time
T_s = oscilloscope rise time

Example

A signal with a rise time of 20 ns is applied to an oscilloscope which also has a rise of 20 ns. Calculate the approximate rise time of the displayed signal on the screen.

Solution

Since $T_p = T_s$, and $T_p = \sqrt{(T_m{}^2 - T_s{}^2)}$ then
$T_p = \sqrt{(T_m{}^2 - T_p{}^2)}$ and
$T_p{}^2 = T_m{}^2 - T_p{}^2$

i.e., $T_m{}^2 = 2\,T_p{}^2$
$T_m = \sqrt{2\,T_p}$
$T_m\ 1.414\,T_p$
But $T_p = T_s = 20$ ns, thus
$T_m = 1.414 \times 20$
$= 28$ ns.

Measurement of duty cycle

Another important aspect of pulse applications is the pulse width expressed as a percentage of the period of the waveform. This is known as the *duty cycle*, i.e.,

$$\text{duty cycle} = \frac{\text{pulse width}}{\text{period}} \times 100\%$$

Both pulse width and period may be found by measuring the respective distances and multiplying each of them by the timebase setting.

If in Fig. 4.16 the timebase setting is 20 μs/cm, thus
pulse width = 1.5 cm × 20 μs/cm = 30 μs
period = 6 × 20 = 120 μs

$$\text{Hence, duty cycle} = \frac{30}{120} \times 100\% = 25\%$$

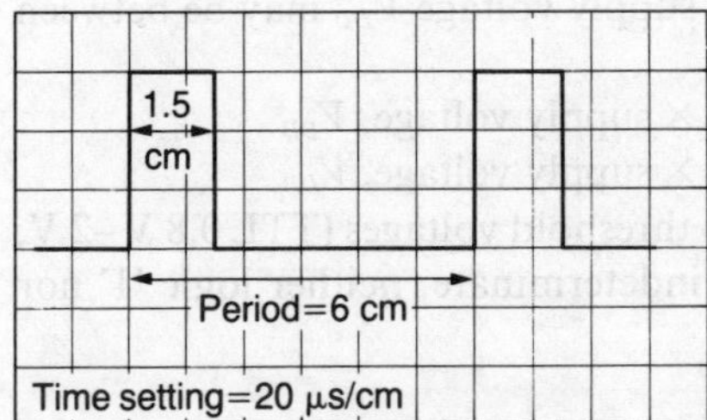

Fig. 4.16 Measure of duty cycle

Alternatively, the duty cycle may be calculated without conversion to time.

$$\text{For example, duty cycle} = \frac{\text{pulse width}}{\text{period}} = \frac{1.5\text{ cm}}{6\text{ cm}} \times 100\% = 25\%.$$

5 Logic state testing instruments

The analogue and digital test instruments considered in the previous chapters are designed to carry out measurements on analogue input signals. This chapter deals with instruments that can test the logic state of inputs, outputs, or any other test point or node in a digital device, board or system. Most modern electronic systems are of the digital type, including, of course, systems that have to process analogue signals, e.g. the DVM. Knowledge of logic state test instruments has become of crucial importance in electronic testing. There are a variety of logic state testers such as the logic probe, the logic pulser and the current tracer. For testing bus structured systems such as a microprocessor based computer, more sophisticated instruments are necessary, such as the logic and signature analysers. The latter are themselves microprocessor controlled systems and will be considered in Chapter 7.

A digital signal has two discrete states: logic '0' represented by a LOW voltage normally 0 V and logic '1' represented by a HIGH voltage. The voltage levels which represent logic '1' depend on the logic technology used. For TTL (transistor-transistor-logic), logic '1' is represented by 5 V, while CMOS logic '1' may vary from 3 V to 15 V. The precise logic threshold voltages to which logic devices will respond are as follows:

For TTL:

logic '1' threshold = 2 V

logic '0' threshold = 0.8 V

For CMOS logic, where the supply voltage V_{DD} may be between 3 V–15 V:

logic '1' threshold = 0.7 × supply voltage, V_{DD}

logic '0' threshold = 0.3 × supply voltage, V_{DD}

A logic level between the two threshold voltages (TTL 0.8 V –2 V, CMOS 0.3 V_{DD} –0.7 V_{DD}) is indeterminate, neither logic '1' nor logic '0'.

The Logic Probe

The logic probe is a logic test instrument which investigates the logic state of any node in a digital circuit, a node being an interconnection between two or more logic devices. It can indicate the presence of a logic '1', logic '0' or an open circuit. Figure 5.1 shows a typical logic probe. Figure 5.2 shows a block diagram for a logic probe. The d.c. supply to the probe is obtained from the circuit to be tested by connecting the probe power leads to the d.c.

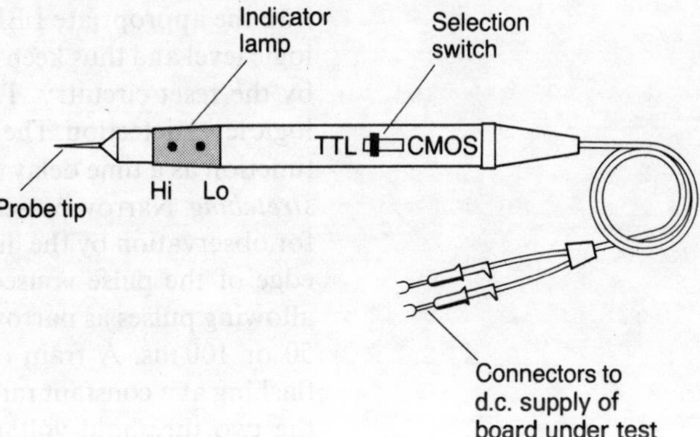

Fig. 5.1 A typical logic probe

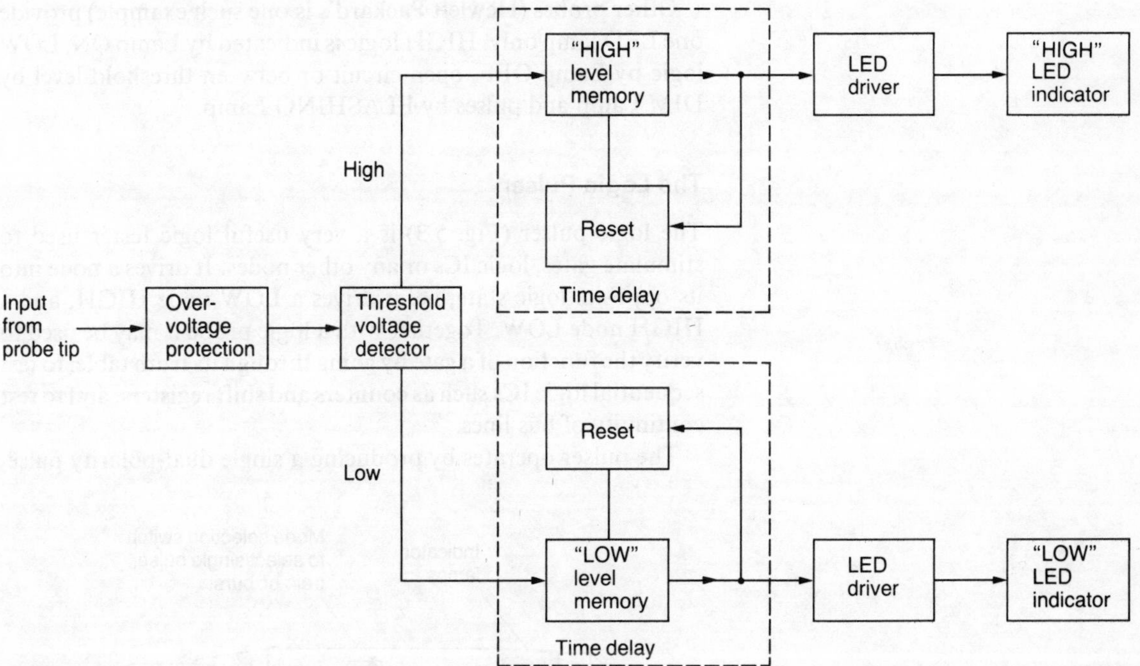

Fig. 5.2 A typical probe block diagram

supply lines of the board under test (BUT). The input to the probe is obtained by placing the tip of the probe in contact with the node to be investigated. The input logic level is fed through an over-voltage protection circuit into the threshold detector. The threshold detector is set to the appropriate level for TTL or CMOS either manually by a switch, or automatically by the circuit itself. The threshold setting is TTL 0.8 V and 2.0 V and CMOS 30% and 70% of the d.c. supply for logic '0' and logic '1' respectively.

When the threshold level is detected, it is then fed into the appropriate memory: the HIGH memory for logic '1' and the LOW memory for logic '0'. The logic state is then captured and fed into the appropriate LED via the driver. The memory retains the logic level and thus keeps the LED indicator ON until it is cleared by the reset circuitry. The process is then repeated for another logic level detection. The logic level memory and the reset circuitry function as a time delay circuit to provide what is known as *pulse stretching.* Narrow pulses are too fast to allow the LED to light up for observation by the human eye. To overcome this, the leading edge of the pulse is used to trigger the time delay circuit, thus allowing pulses as narrow as 10 ns to be 'stretched' to as much as 50 or 100 ms. A train of pulses will be indicated by the LED flashing at a constant rate of about 10 Hz. An input level between the two threshold voltages will give no indication, both LEDs being turned off. This is also true for an open circuited node.

Other probes (Hewlett Packard's is one such example) provide one LED lamp only. HIGH logic is indicated by Lamp ON, LOW logic by Lamp OFF, open circuit or between threshold level by DIM Lamp and pulses by FLASHING Lamp.

The Logic Pulser

The logic pulser (Fig. 5.3) is a very useful logic tester used to stimulate gates, logic ICs or any other nodes. It drives a node into its opposite logic state, i.e. it drives a LOW node HIGH, and a HIGH node LOW. Together with a logic probe it may be used to verify the function of a gate by going through its truth table; to test sequential logic ICs such as counters and shift registers, and to test continuity of bus lines.

The pulser operates by producing a single dual-polarity pulse,

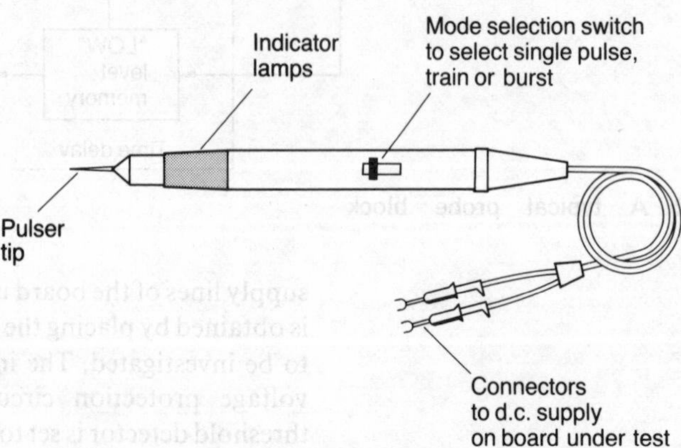

Fig. 5.3 A typical logic pulser

shown in Fig. 5.4(a). When the pulser output tip is connected to a node, it will drive it into a HIGH or a LOW depending on the original logic state of the node. If the node is originally LOW, then the pulser output has no effect while it is LOW. However, when it changes to HIGH, it takes the node with it (Fig. 5.4(b)). The opposite is true when the node is originally HIGH, see Fig. 5.4(c). The voltage levels shown in Fig. 5.4 are the threshold voltages for TTL technology. For CMOS, the threshold voltages must be adjusted accordingly.

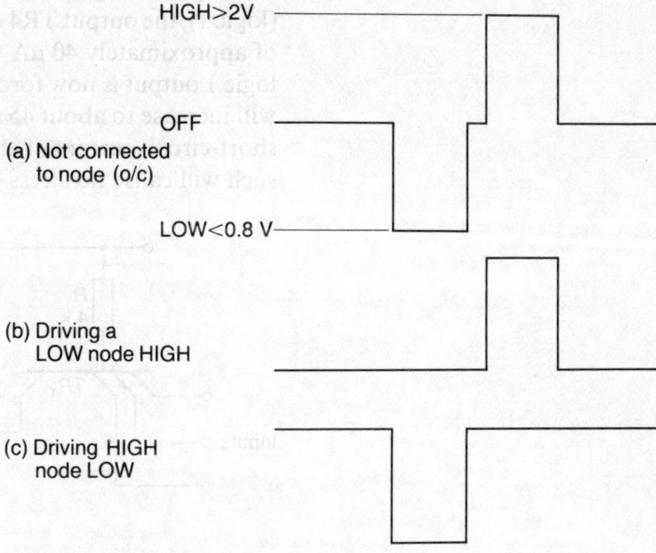

Fig. 5.4 Logic pulser outputs

Backdriving stress

In a circuit, each component is connected to some other components, so that forcing the input of a component under test HIGH or LOW may require driving another component's output HIGH or LOW as well. This output driving is known as backdriving, and may cause stress on the digital IC.

Figure 5.5 shows a gate G3 which is to be tested by a logic pulser. The component under test G3 is fed with the output of two NAND gates G1 and G2. Before any gate can be tested by the pulser (or by any other functional tester), power must be applied to the entire circuit. When power is applied, all nodes and the outputs

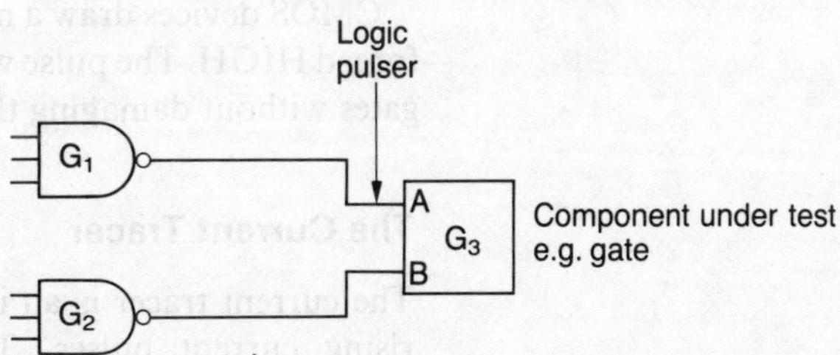

Fig. 5.5

and inputs of all gates will assume some initial state (HIGH or LOW). In testing G3 the logic pulser may be used to cause input A of G3 to change its initial logic state. In doing so, the output of NAND gate G1 is also caused to change its initial state. In other words, the output of G1 is backdriven by the pulser. A stress may therefore occur on G1 which may damage the gate. Note that the component under test, i.e. G3, does not come under any stress due to the action of the pulser. In order to understand the type of stress caused on NAND gate G1, the circuit of a NAND gate must be investigated. Figure 5.6 shows a TTL NAND gate. For a HIGH (logic 1), the output TR4 conducts since TR3 is OFF and a current of approximately 40 μA will flow into G3. It is found that if this logic 1 output is now forced to go LOW (logic 0), then the current will increase to about 45 mA. This current is well below the rated short-circuit current of about 70 mA for this type of circuit, and as such will cause no stress on the gate.

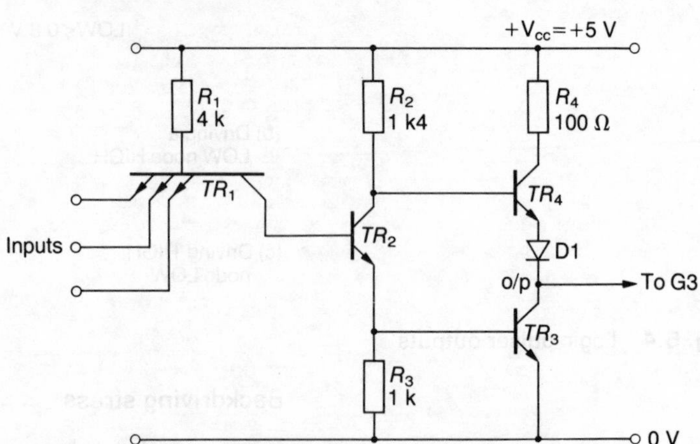

Fig. 5.6 TTL NAND gate circuit diagram

The stress occurs when a LOW output is driven HIGH. For a LOW (logic 0) output TR3 conducts since TR4 is OFF and a current of about 1.6 mA flows from G3 into TR3. Forcing the output to go HIGH will cause a very large current (about 160 mA) to flow into TR3, more than twice as large as the rated short-circuit current. If such a current is sustained, then the gate will be damaged. For this reason, the pulse width of the pulser is chosen to be very narrow, in the region of 5 μs to ensure that no damage is inflicted by backdriving.

CMOS devices draw a much smaller current when the output is forced HIGH. The pulse width may therefore be wider for CMOS gates without damaging the gate.

The Current Tracer

The current tracer is an instrument which tests the flow of fast-rising current pulses. The tracer senses the magnetic field generated by these digital signals in the circuit and indicates its presence by a light indicator such as a LED.

The tracer may be used with a logic pulser to identify short circuits to earth, or to d.c. supply lines or between lines or nodes.

The current tracer is an additional testing tool which takes over where the probe leaves off. The logic probe may identify a 'bad' node, e.g. stuck-at-one or stuck-at-zero. However, the cause of the fault cannot be identified by the probe itself. For example in Fig. 5.7 where Unit 2 pin 9 is shorted to earth giving a stuck-at-zero condition. The logic probe will indicate LOW, regardless of the input. A pulser is then used at U1 pin 2 to see if the state of the pin may be changed. When this proves unsuccessful, the tracer is used to follow the current path from U1 pin 2 to U2 pin 9 where an earth (or sink) exists.

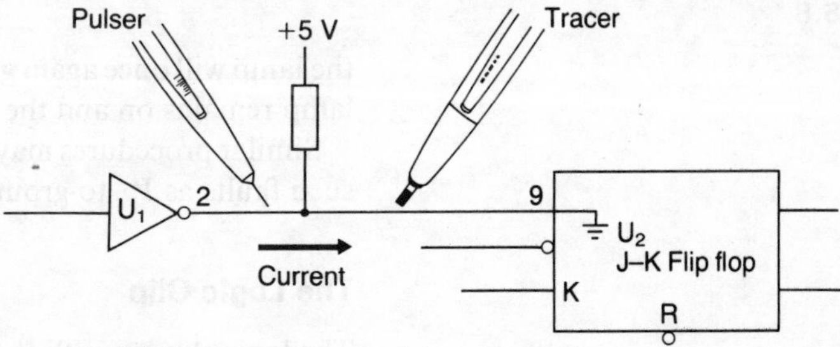

Fig. 5.7

Setting up the tracer

1. Align the tracer's tip to a reference point, normally the output of a driver, e.g. a pulser.
2. Set the sensitivity control (if provided) to indicate the presence of a signal current by an appropriate lamp brightness.
3. Move the tracer along the track, observing the brightness of the indicating light. As the tracer is moved around the circuit, the lamp brightness may change. An increase in brightness indicates an increase in current, while a reduced brightness indicates a reduced current.
4. Follow the path that sustains lamp brightness at the same level. When the fault is found, the lamp will be as bright as it was at the reference point.

Multiple Input Fault

Figure 5.8 shows a shorted input at U5 in a multiple input circuit. Initially, the logic probe will indicate a stuck-at-zero condition at the output of U1, node A. By pulsing this node as shown, a current path then exists towards the faulty node F. The current tracer is then moved from node A to node B. If it is taken towards node E, the lamp will dim, since there is no current between B and E. At node C, the lamp will be on. If the tracer is moved towards node G,

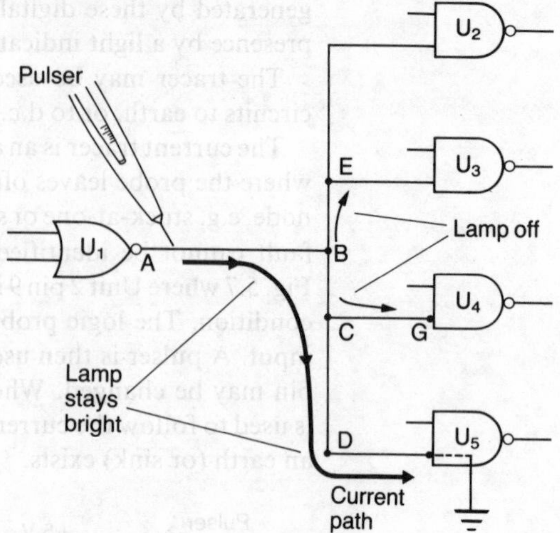

Fig. 5.8

the lamp will once again go off. Moving along to D and then F, the lamp remains on and the faulty node identified.

Similar procedures may be followed for a solder bridge fault and such faults as V_{cc} to ground faults.

The Logic Clip

The logic clip is another device that can indicate the logic state of an IC pin. In this case, the clip reads the states of all pins simultaneously. The state of each pin is indicated by a LED: ON for logic 1 and OFF for logic 0. A pulse is indicated by a dimmed LED. Figure 5.9 shows a block diagram for one of the IC pins. The decision logic network distinguishes between V_{cc}, ground and a logic pin. The output is fed into the threshold detector and then amplified to drive the LED.

The logic clip may be used to verify the truth table of an IC and to test a counter or a shift register for faults on outputs, resets, clears or other signals.

The Logic Comparator

The logic comparator compares the logic state of an IC pin with the logic state produced by a known-good IC. It repeats this test for all the pins and displays any errors in performance pin by pin. The comparator can perform an in-circuit test on a suspected IC

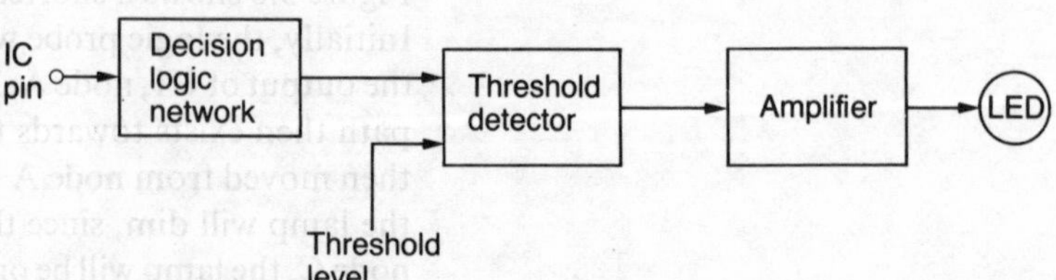

Fig. 5.9 Logic-clip block diagram for one pin

very quickly and efficiently. The disadvantage is that a known-good IC must be available.

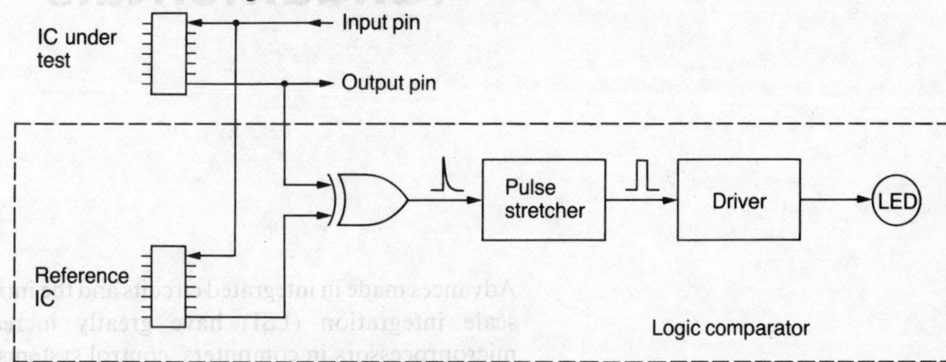

Fig. 5.10 Logic comparator block diagram

Figure 5.10 shows a block diagram for a logic comparator. The appropriate reference IC is first inserted into the available socket in the comparator. Each input pin of the reference IC is connected in parallel with the IC in the circuit under test. In this way, both ICs receive identical input signals. Each output pin of the reference IC is connected to an EXCLUSIVE-OR gate. (The block diagram shows the connections for one input and one output pin only.) The other input to the EXCLUSIVE-OR gate comes from the output pin of the IC under test. The EXCLUSIVE-OR gate therefore compares the signals fed into it from the two output pins. If they are identical, the gate output is zero and the LED remains off. However, when the two signals are different, the gate produces an output as shown in Fig. 5.11. An error is indicated whether a pulse is missing completely or merely delayed. The error indicating pulse from the EXCLUSIVE-OR, which may be as short as 200 ns, is fed into a pulse stretcher before being fed into the driver amplifier and subsequently to the LED.

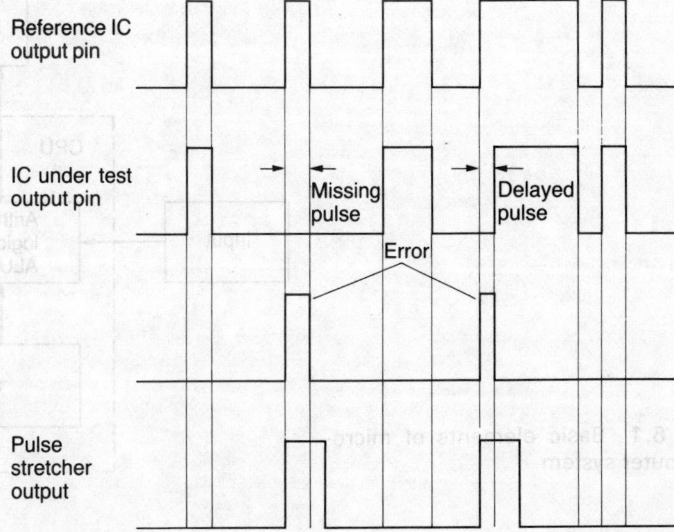

Fig. 5.11 Timing diagram for a logic comparator

6 Microprocessor fundamentals

Advances made in integrated circuits and the introduction of large-scale integration (LSI) have greatly increased the use of microprocessors in computers, control systems and instruments. An understanding of microprocessor fundamentals has become an essential requirement in modern-day electronics. For the purposes of this book, a knowledge of microprocessor systems is necessary, both in terms of understanding modern microprocessor-based instruments such as logging devices and automatic test equipment, as well as to develop effective fault-finding techniques for a variety of microprocessor-based systems.

The Microprocessor-Based Computer (Microcomputer) System

The basic elements of a microcomputer system are shown in Fig. 6.1. It consists of four fundamental units. The central processing unit (CPU), also known as the microprocessor unit (MPU), contains two further units, the arithmetical and logical, and the control units. At the heart of the system is the arithmetical and

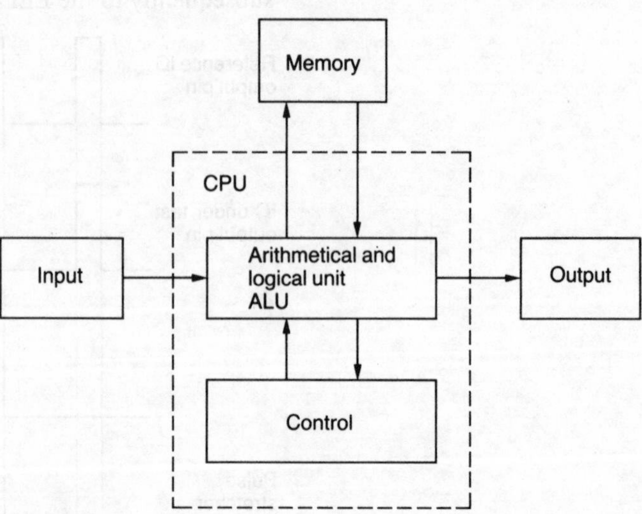

Fig. 6.1 Basic elements of microcomputer system

logical unit (ALU), which communicates with all other four units. The ALU carries out various operations in accordance with a set of instructions known as a programme, stored in memory. The ALU may receive data from the input unit or send data out via the output unit, in accordance with the programme. It may also store data into memory for temporary storage. The whole process is synchronized by the control unit which is responsible for the timing of each instruction and the flow of data within the ALU as well as between the ALU and other units.

Memory

There are two main types of memory chips. The read-only memory (ROM) is a permanent data store. The data is entered into ROM at the manufacturing stage, and remains there permanently. The CPU can only READ from ROM. It *cannot write* into it, i.e. it cannot change the data stored in ROM. The second main type of memory is the random access memory (RAM). Data is stored in RAM temporarily, and may be changed by the CPU. The CPU can thus READ the data stored in RAM as well as WRITE new data into it. Unless a back-up battery is used, the data stored in RAM will be wiped out when the power supply is turned off. This is why such memory is called *volatile*. ROM, on the other hand, retains its data even when the supply is off. Such a memory is called *non-volatile*. There are other types of memory chips, namely the programmable ROM (PROM) into which data may be written by the user to be stored permanently, and the erasable PROM (EPROM) whose data may be erased and new information entered by the user.

Microcomputer architecture

Figure 6.2 shows the architecture or organization of a micro-

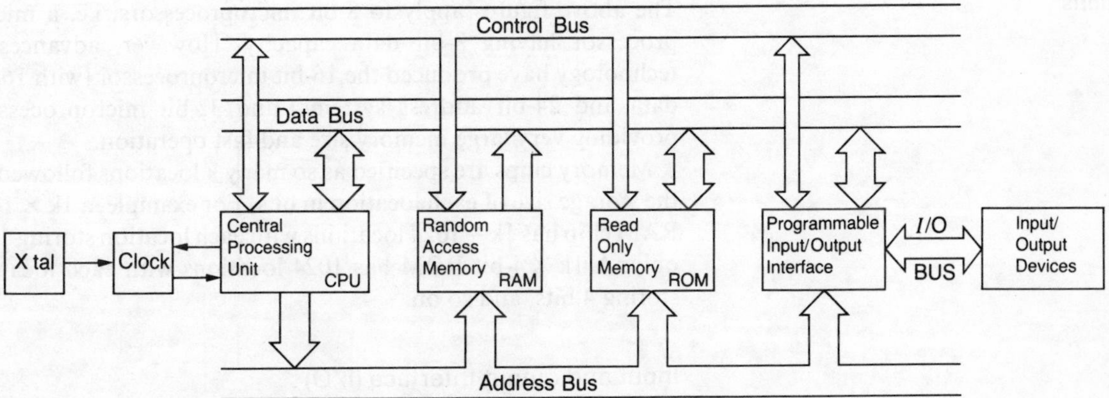

Fig. 6.2 Microcomputer system architecture

computer system. It shows the manner in which the various elements are connected to each other in a typical microprocessor computer system. The microprocessor CPU is a single LSI or very large scale integration (VLSI) chip containing all necessary circuitry to interpret and execute programme instructions in terms of data manipulation, logic and arithmetic operations and timing and control of the system.

Microprocessors are normally mounted as a 40-pin dual-in-line (DIL) package, as shown in Fig. 6.3.

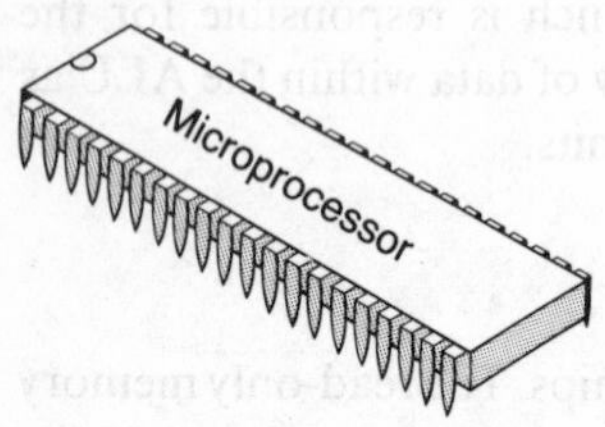

Fig. 6.3 The microprocessor IC chip

Memory organization

The memory unit consists of a number of memory *locations* where data in the form of digital bits may be stored. Each location can normally store an 8-bit (one-byte) binary number. Each location has a unique 16-bit (2-byte), *address*, as shown in Fig. 6.4, starting from the hexadecimal numbers 0000 to FFFF. The high-byte bits 8 to 15 (the two HEX numbers at the left-hand side) is known as the page. For example, address 002F is on page 00 (zero page), while 2B03 is on page 2B. For a 16-bit address system there are a maximum of $2^{16} = 65\,536$ addressable locations made up from $2^8 = 256$ pages of memory, with each page containing $2^8 = 256$ locations. Memory size is normally quoted using the binary kilo with symbol k where

$$1\text{k (memory)} = 2^{10} = 1024 \text{ locations.}$$

It follows, therefore, that in a 16-bit address system there are

$$2^{16} = 2^6 \times 2^{10} = 64\text{k of memory.}$$

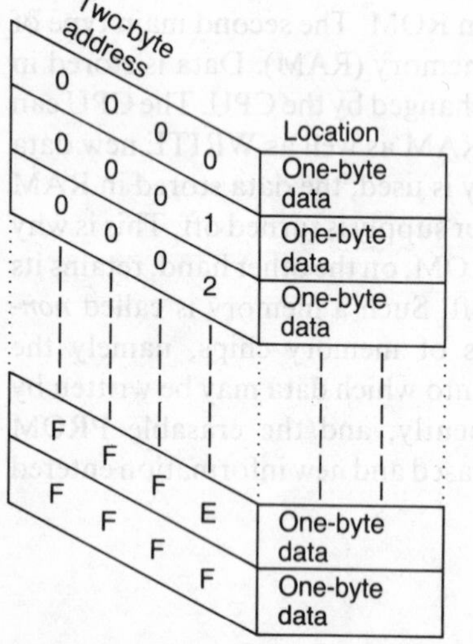

Fig. 6.4 Addressed memory locations

For an 8-bit data system where each memory location can store an 8-bit or one-byte word, there is a maximum memory storage of

$$64\text{k (memory)} \times 8 \text{ bits} = 64\text{k bytes.}$$

The above figures apply to 8-bit microprocessors, i.e. a microprocessor having 8-bit data capacity. However, advances in technology have produced the 16-bit microprocessor (with 16-bit data and 24-bit address systems) and 32-bit microprocessors providing very large memory size and fast operation.

Memory chips are specified as so many k locations followed by the storage size of each location in bits. For example, a 1k × 1-bit RAM chip has 1k = 1024 locations with each location storing 1 bit only. A 1k × 4-bit ROM has 1024 locations with each location storing 4 bits, and so on.

Input and output interface (I/O)

The I/O interface unit connects the microcomputer to external devices. It acts as an input or an output route for transferring data to or from the microprocessor and external devices such as keyboards, display devices, transducers or drive circuitry for electromechanical devices such as stepper motors or relays. The interface is programmable, i.e. each terminal port may be set to act as an input or an output by the microprocessor control.

The buses

The main hardware elements in a microcomputer described above are interconnected with each other by what is known as a *bus structure*. A bus is a group of connecting wires or tracks used as paths for digital information that have a common function. There are three main buses in a microcomputer: the data bus, the address bus and the control bus. The *data bus* is used to transfer data between the microprocessor and the other elements in the system. It is normally a bi-directional 8-bit bus.

The *address bus* is used to send the address of memory locations either to retrieve data, i.e. READ from RAM or ROM, or to store or WRITE data into addressed locations. It is also used to address the Input/Output Unit which may be involved in data transfer. The address bus is uni-directional, carrying 16 bits of digital information simultaneously.

The *control bus* is used to send control signals from the microprocessor to the other elements of the system. The number of control lines on the bus depends both on the microprocessor used and the design of the system. The main control signals are as follows:

The clock

A master clock is used in a microcomputer to synchronize the movement of data. This is achieved by using a high speed crystal controlled pulse generator. The speed of the clock determines the speed of operation of the microcomputer.

Read/writes

The microprocessor must determine the direction of data to or from the CPU. In a READ operation, the transfer is from memory to the microprocessor, while in a WRITE operation, the transfer is from the microprocessor to memory. Two separate control lines, one for READ and one for WRITE, are sometimes used.

Interrupts

When a peripheral device, e.g. a printer, needs attention, the main programme may be interrupted temporarily by the interrupt control line. After servicing the peripheral device, the microprocessor returns to the original programme at the point where it was interrupted. There are several types of interrupts, e.g. interrupt request (IRQ), where the processor will complete the current instruction that is being executed before recognizing the interrupt, while other interrupts are taken immediately by the microprocessor.

Reset

This is a type of interrupt which stops the microprocessor programme. When the reset pin is activated, the microprocessor performs a sequence of operations halting programming execution and clearing its internal registers. It then places a specific address on the address bus known as the reset address where the first instruction of the start-up programme may be found. The start-up programme, which is stored in ROM, sets up the microprocessor and all other units, e.g. keyboard, VDU, RAM, ready for use. The Zilog Z80 and Intel 8080 use reset address 0000. Other microprocessors, such as the 6502 or the Motorola MC 6800, use two addresses known as vectors, which contain the low and high bytes of the address where the first instruction of the start-up programme is stored. The MC 6800 uses FFFE and FFFF as the two vectors, while the 6502 uses FFFC and FFFD.

General Operation of a Basic Microcomputer

The microcomputer operates on a *Fetch* and *Execute* basis. During the fetch phase, the microprocessor receives the instruction from the memory location where the programme is stored. This is carried out by the microprocessor placing the appropriate address of memory location on the address bus, and activating the READ control line. The appropriate memory chip will then place the contents of that location, i.e. the instruction in the form of an operation code (OP code), on the data bus which the microprocessor will receive and store into an internal register known as the *Instruction Register.* During the execute phase the microprocessor having received the instruction OP code, will then decode it and generate the necessary timing and control signals to execute the instruction. When that instruction is completed the microprocessor will then place the next programme address, i.e. the address where the next instruction is stored, on to the address bus. Figure 6.5 shows the connections between the microprocessor and its memory chips. A 1k memory chip (ROM or RAM) requires 10 address lines A0–A9 only. Address lines A10–A12 are used to select one of eight individual 1k memory chips giving a total of 8k memory. For a larger memory store other address lines (A13, A14 and A15) have to be used. The selection is carried out by the *chip select decoder or address decoder.* The truth table for the address

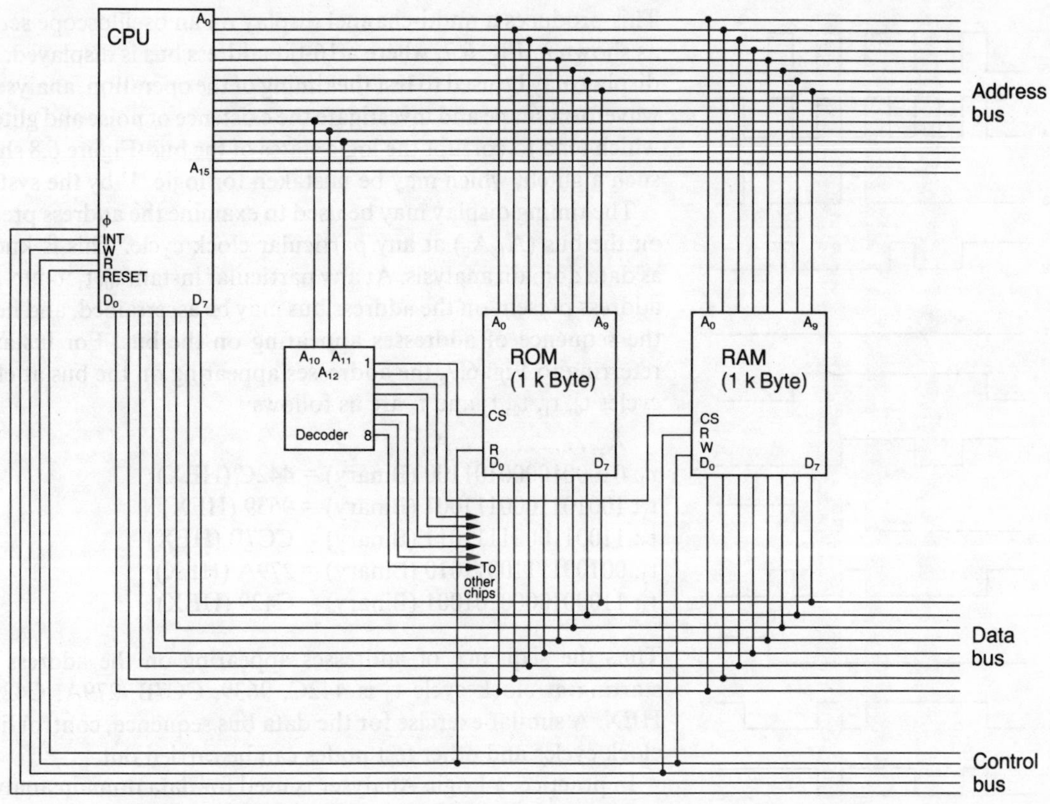

Fig. 6.5 Connections between the CPU and its memory chips

A_{12}	A_{11}	A_{10}	Chip selected
0	0	0	Chip 1
0	0	1	Chip 2
0	1	0	Chip 3
0	1	1	Chip 4
1	0	0	Chip 5
1	0	1	Chip 6
1	1	0	Chip 7
1	1	1	Chip 8

Fig. 6.6 Truth table for address decoder in Fig. 6.5

decoder is shown in Fig. 6.6. The memory chips RAM and ROM are also connected to the data bus D0–D7. In the case of ROM, the connection is unidirectional where data may only be read from memory. For RAM, the data connection is bidirectional, where the CPU may READ from and WRITE into the RAM chip. Hence the need for the READ, R, and WRITE, W, control line connections.

Time and Data Domain Analysis

There are two ways of examining the logic states of a test node on a bus line: the time domain and the data domain. The time domain is where the waveform at the node is examined normally by the use of an oscilloscope. Monitoring one single node, e.g. an address line, at a time is obviously inadequate for any form of analysis of the operation of the system. It is the relationship between all the address lines, whereby the complete address word can be ascertained, that is essential for any form of analysis. Time domain analysis, therefore, involves looking at a number of nodes simultaneously, e.g. 16 address lines, 8 data lines or control lines.

This produces a multi-channel display on an oscilloscope screen, as shown in Fig. 6.7, where a 16-bit address bus is displayed. The display may be used to test the timing of the operation, analyse the waveform shape and investigate the existence of noise and glitches which tend to corrupt the logic states of the bus. Figure 6.8 shows such a glitch, which may be mistaken for logic '1' by the system.

The timing display may be used to examine the address present on the bus ($A_{15}A_0$) at any particular clock cycle. This is known as data domain analysis. At any particular instant t_0, t_1, t_2 etc., the address present on the address bus may be ascertained, and hence the sequence of addresses appearing on the bus. For instance, referring to Fig. 6.7, the addresses appearing on the bus at clock cycles t_0, t_1, t_2, t_3 and t_4 are as follows:

A_{15}. . . . . .A_0
t_0: 0100010000101100 (Binary) = 442C (HEX)
t_1: 1001011000111001 (Binary) = 9639 (HEX)
t_2: 1100110001111011 (Binary) = CC7B (HEX)
t_3: 0010011110011010 (Binary) = 279A (HEX)
t_4: 1100010000101001 (Binary) = C429 (HEX)

Thus the sequence of addresses appearing on the address bus starting at clock cycle t_0 is 442C, 9639, CC7B, 279A, C429 in HEX. A similar exercise for the data bus sequence, control lines, clock cycles and other test nodes can be carried out.

In practice, a Logic Analyser is used for data domain analysis, where the sequence of words present on a bus (address or data or both) are presented in binary or hex, as will be explained in Chapter 7.

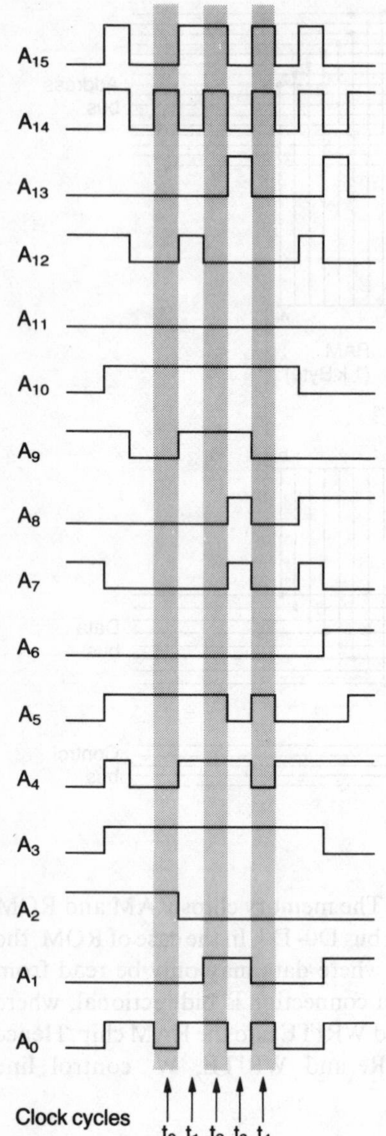

Fig. 6.7 Address bus waveforms

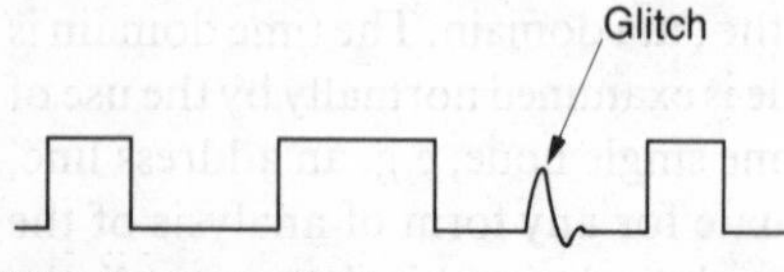

Fig. 6.8 A glitch

Machine Code Programming

The microprocessor carries out its operations according to a programme. The programme is a set of instructions which breaks down each operation into a series of individual tasks which the microprocessor performs step by step. These instructions are fed into the microprocessor in the form of a code known as machine code or OP Code. Each different make of microprocessor chip has its own set of machine codes known as its *instruction set.* The machine code is a binary word, although normally it is given in hexadecimal for easy handling. The data operated upon by the microprocessor is known as the *operand.* Machine code programming is the fundamental form of programming, which may be fed directly into the microprocessor chip. Other forms of programming using mnemonics (an easy to remember alphabetical code derived from the instruction itself) or higher levels of programming such as BASIC require an assembler to convert these programmes into the appropriate binary codes that the microprocessor can understand.

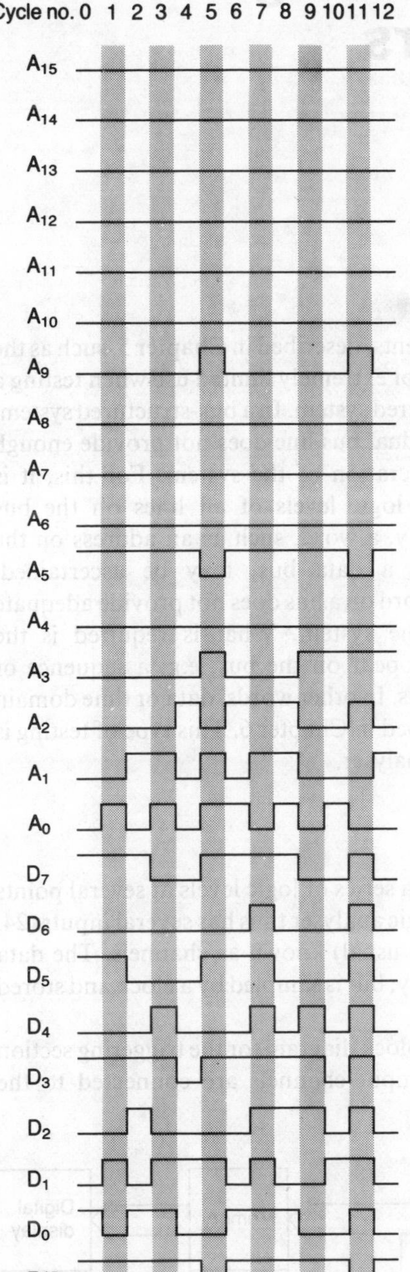

Fig. 6.9 Time domain analysis of a microcomputer system

Consider the following simple programme, which stores data AA_{HEX} and FF_{HEX} in locations $021B_{HEX}$ and $021C_{HEX}$. Assuming we are using a 6502 microprocessor, then the programme will be as shown below, starting at programme address 0030:

Programme Address (HEX)	*Mnemonic*	*OP Code (HEX)*	*Operand (HEX)*	*Comments*
0030	LDA #	A9		Load accumulator with data following immediately
0031			AA	Data
0032	STA	8D		Store accumulator contents in address location given in next 2 bytes
0033			1B	Low byte of address
0034			02	High byte of address
0035	LDA #	A9		Load accumulator with data following immediately
0036			FF	Data
0037	STA	8D		Store contents of accumulator in address location in the next 2 bytes
0038			1C	Low byte of address
0039			02	High byte of address
003A	BRK	00		Break or halt

The address, data and the state $R/\overline{W}$ control line are represented by the simultaneous logic states at each cycle. For instance at cycle no. 3 address lines A_{15}–A_0 may be read off the time domain display as 0000000000110011 (BINARY) giving an address in HEX of 0033. Similarly for the data bus lines, at cycle no. 3 the data lines D7–D0 are read off the display as 00011011 (BINARY) giving data 1B in HEX. Finally $R/\overline{W}$ waveform gives a logic 1 for cycle no. 3. In other words, cycle no. 3 is a READ cycle.

7 Logic and signature analysers

Logic state testing instruments, described in Chapter 5, such as the logic probe or IC clip, are of extremely limited use when testing a microprocessor bus-structured system. In a bus-structured system, the logic level of an individual bus line does not provide enough information about the operation of the system. For this, it is necessary to look at the logic levels of all lines on the bus simultaneously. In this way, a word, such as an address on the address bus or data on a data bus, may be ascertained. Furthermore, one single word on a bus does not provide adequate test information about the system. What is required is the sequence of words that appear on the bus, e.g. a sequence of addresses on the address bus. In other words, data or time domain testing is needed, as described in Chapter 6. This type of testing is carried out using a logic analyser.

The Logic Analyser

The logic analyser records a series of logic levels at several points on a unit under test. The logic analyser thus has several inputs (24, 32, 48 or more being quite usual) known as channels. The data is not recorded continuously, but is sampled by a clock and stored in memory.

Figure 7.1 shows a basic block diagram for the triggering section of a logic analyser. The input channels are connected to the

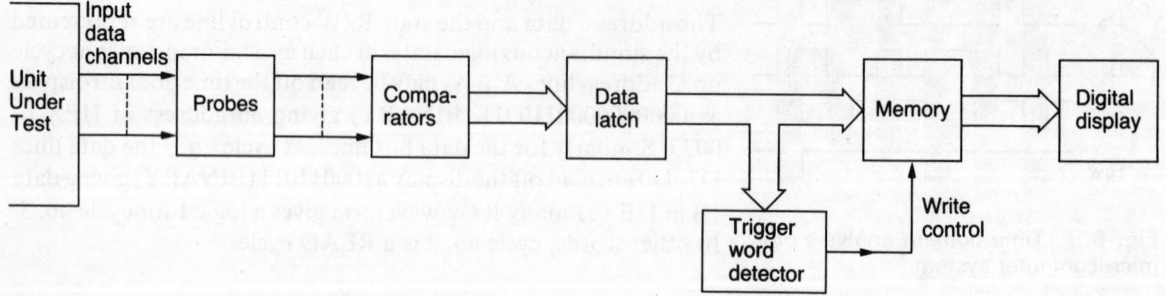

Fig. 7.1 Logic analyser triggering section

appropriate test points, e.g. in an 8-bit microprocessor system, 16 channels may be connected to the address bus, 8 channels to the data bus and others to the control lines. After passing through the probes and comparators, the input data is fed into the data latch, where the logic levels of each channel are 'held' long enough for the analyser to accurately capture the information. This data is fed into the memory block which may store the data for later display. The memory block is activated to capture and store the data by the write control from the trigger word detector. The trigger word detector is preloaded with a trigger word representing a combination of the simultaneous logic states of the input channels. The stream of input data is fed into the trigger word detector as shown. When the detector recognizes the preloaded trigger word occurring in the input channels, it enables the Write control. The memory then stores a block of data activity before and after the occurrence of the trigger word. For example, consider the simple programme in the previous chapter which stores data AA_{HEX} and FF_{HEX} in locations $021B_{HEX}$ and $021C_{HEX}$ (see p 71).

In order to test the correct operation of the programme, it is required to look at the sequence of addresses that appear on the address bus. To do this, a 16-channel logic analyser is used with the input channels connected to the address bus. Before the logic analyser can capture any data, a trigger word has to be chosen and loaded into the instrument. The trigger word must be an address that appears on the bus when the programme is running. Any of the addresses shown in the table on page 71 may be used, that is 0030, 0031, 0032 ... 021B ... 003A etc.

The easiest trigger word to choose is a programme address, such as 0034. The trigger word detector is then loaded with the chosen trigger word 0034 and the programme is run. A sequence of addresses will then occur on the address bus to be fed into memory and the trigger word detector. When the trigger word 0034 occurs on the address bus, the detector recognizes it and the write control instructs the memory to capture and store a block of addresses before and after the trigger word. (The size of the block stored is determined by the size of the memory.) When that happens, the logic analyser displays the sequence of addresses captured for examination. The display in this example is as shown in Table 7.1. The cursor shows the position of any address in relation to the trigger word which appears at cursor 00. Addresses occurring before the trigger word are given negative cursor numbers, while those occurring after the trigger word are given positive cursor numbers. The complete address sequence occurring on the address bus for the programme is available for close examination. The captured data may also be displayed in binary form where the logic state of each address line is indicated. If a wrong trigger word is chosen, i.e. an address that does not occur on the bus, the logic analyser will not trigger and the display remains blank.

Table 7.1

	Cursor	*HEX*	*Binary*
		DATA DISPLAYED	
	−08	Random	
	−07	Random	
	−06	Random	
	−05	Random	A_{15}......................A_0
	−04	0030	0000 0000 0011 0000
	−03	0031	0000 0000 0011 0001
	−02	0032	0000 0000 0011 0010
	−01	0033	0000 0000 0011 0011
Trigger word	**00**	**0034**	**0000 0000 0011 0100**
	+01	021B	0000 0010 0001 1011
	+02	0035	0000 0000 0011 0101
	+03	0036	0000 0000 0011 0110
	+04	0037	0000 0000 0011 0111
	+05	0038	0000 0000 0011 1000
	+06	0039	0000 0000 0011 1001
	+07	021C	0000 0010 0001 1100
	+08	003A	0000 0000 0011 1010
	+09	Start of break subroutine	

Note: **The break subroutine has been neglected for simplicity. In practice, at the ninth cursor count, a subroutine is called and executed.**

To display the information on the data bus, a further eight input channels are required, a total of 24 channels. Sixteen input channels are connected to the address bus and eight channels to the data bus. The trigger word has to be one which represents a combination of the logic states of all input channels at any time cycle. Using the same address as in the previous example, namely 0034, and referring to the table on page 71 shows that the data associated with that address is 02. Hence the trigger word is 003402. Other trigger words may be used such as 021BAA or 00381C. The input data to the logic analyser will be captured and stored in the same way as the addresses, with the display showing the logic levels of 24 test points or six hexadecimal digits, as shown in Table 7.2.

Timing analysis

Once the input data has been captured and stored in memory, it may be displayed as logic levels in the form of waveforms for time domain analysis. Timing analysis involves displaying the waveforms of the input channel simultaneously. These waveforms are produced from the digital data stored in the memory of the analyser by the use of a digital-to-analogue converter, as shown in Fig. 7.2. The D-A converter modifies the digital data to produce a

Table 7.2

	DISPLAY				
	Cursor Count	*HEXADECIMAL Address*	*Data*	*BINARY Address*	*Data*
	−07	Random	Random	Random	Random
	−05	Random	Random	Random	Random
	−04	0030	A9	0000 0000 0011 0000	1010 1001
	−03	0031	AA	0000 0000 0011 0001	1010 1010
	−02	0032	8D	0000 0000 0011 0010	1000 1101
	−01	0033	1B	0000 0000 0011 0011	0001 1011
Trigger word	**00**	**0034**	**02**	**0000 0000 0011 0100**	**0000 0010**
	+01	021B	AA	0000 0010 0001 1011	1010 1010
	+02	0035	A9	0000 0000 0011 0101	1010 1001
	+03	0036	FF	0000 0000 0011 0110	1111 1111
	+04	0037	8D	0000 0000 0011 0111	1000 1101
	+05	0038	1C	0000 0000 0011 1000	0001 1100
	+06	0039	02	0000 0000 0011 1001	0000 0010
	+07	021C	FF	0000 0010 0001 1100	1111 1111
	+08	003A	00	0000 0000 0011 1010	0000 0000
	+09	Break subroutine		Break subroutine	

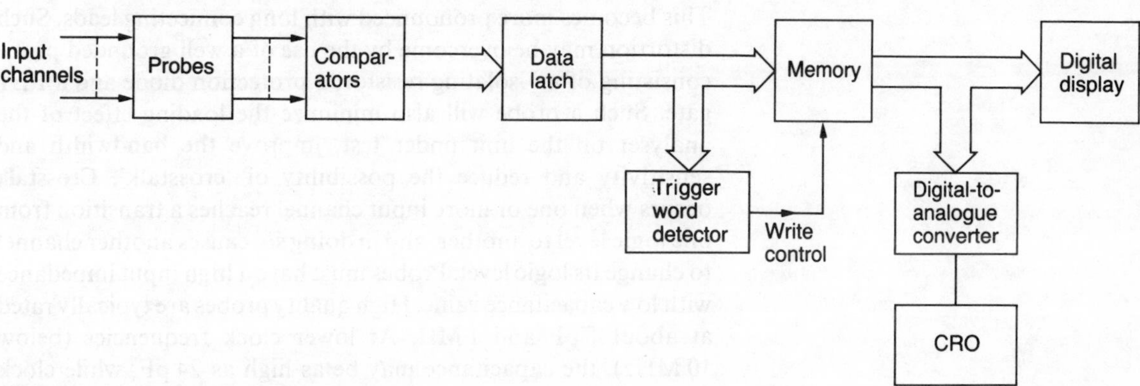

Fig. 7.2 The use of a digital-to-analogue converter for timing display

multi-channel display on an oscilloscope. A typical timing display is shown in Fig. 7.3.

Probes and comparators

Unlike measurements of analogue signals, in digital state analysis, an error in recognizing a single bit in one channel is sufficient to render the whole analysis useless. It is essential, therefore, that the logic level of each input bit is accurately recognized and correctly

Fig. 7.3 A typical logic analyser timing display

converted into a logic state. To do this, probes and comparators are used, as shown in Fig. 7.4.

Direct connection between these nodes on the unit under test and the analyser, results in distorted pulse waveforms in the form of rounding off leading and trailing edges as shown in Fig. 7.5. This becomes more pronounced with long connecting leads. Such distortion may be overcome by the use of a well grounded probe consisting of an isolating resistor, a protection diode and a FET gate. Such a probe will also minimize the loading effect of the analyser on the unit under test, improve the bandwidth and sensitivity and reduce the possibility of 'crosstalk'. **Crosstalk** occurs when one or more input channel reaches a transition from one logic level to another, and in doing so, causes another channel to change its logic level. Probes must have a high input impedance with low capacitance value. High quality probes are typically rated at about 5 pF and 1 MΩ. At lower clock frequencies (below 10 MHz), the capacitance may be as high as 24 pF, while clock

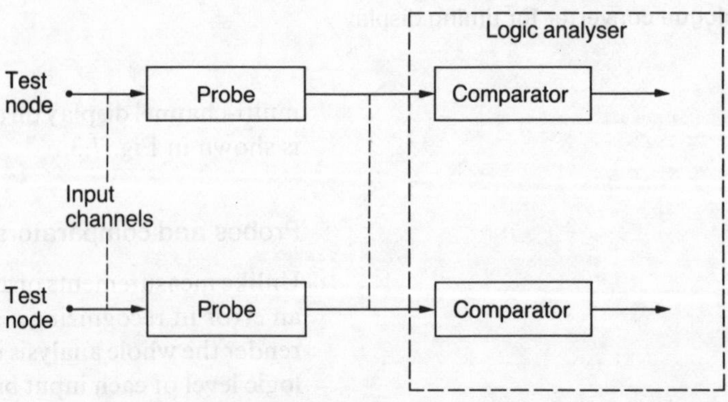

Fig. 7.4

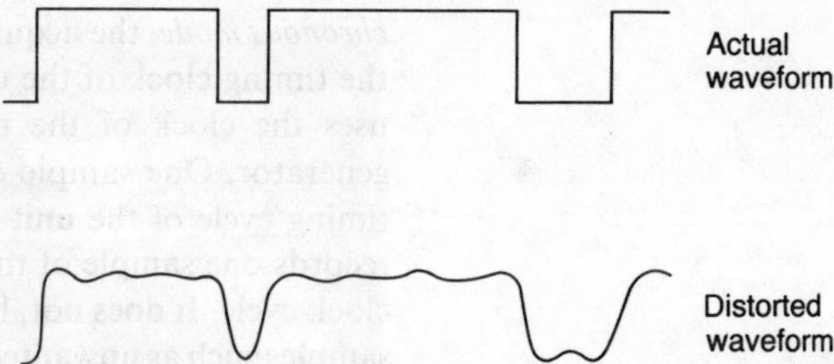

Fig. 7.5

frequencies above 100 MHz require a probe capacitance of as little as 1 pF.

Once a 'clean' pulse waveform has been established by the probe system, the logic state of each bit has to be correctly identified as a HIGH or a LOW. This may be carried out by the probe itself. However, because the probe is external to the analyser, separate comparators are used, as shown in Fig. 7.4. The comparators may be preset to the appropriate threshold voltage determined by the technology used in the unit under test.

Timing and sampling

As explained in Chapter 6, a microprocessor system operates on a fetch and execute cycle. The timing cycle is produced by an internal clock which synchronizes the operation of the system. The logic analyser must therefore capture the information at least once every cycle of the unit under test. The input data is, in fact, sampled at a rate determined by a sampling generator, which resets the latch to receive the next batch of input data, as shown in Fig. 7.6. The latch keeps the data stable for a period of time, long enough for the analyser to identify the logic states accurately. The sampling generator controls the acquisition of the input data by the analyser. There are two modes of operation, namely the **synchronous** mode and the *asynchronous* mode. In the *syn-*

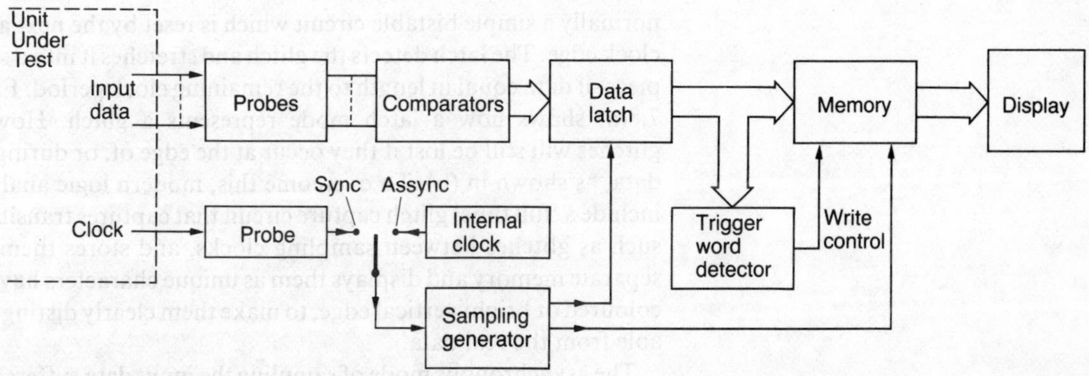

Fig. 7.6 Logic analyser triggering and sampling sections

chronous mode, the acquisition of data occurs synchronously with the timing clock of the unit under test. In this case, the analyser uses the clock of the unit under test to trigger the sampling generator. One sample of the input data is thus taken for each timing cycle of the unit under test. The synchronous mode thus records one sample of the logic states of the input data for every clock cycle. It does not, however, capture anything between these samples such as unwanted glitches, which may affect the operation of the unit under test. Figure 7.7 shows how sampling misses a glitch in an input channel. In the *asynchronous mode*, the analyser

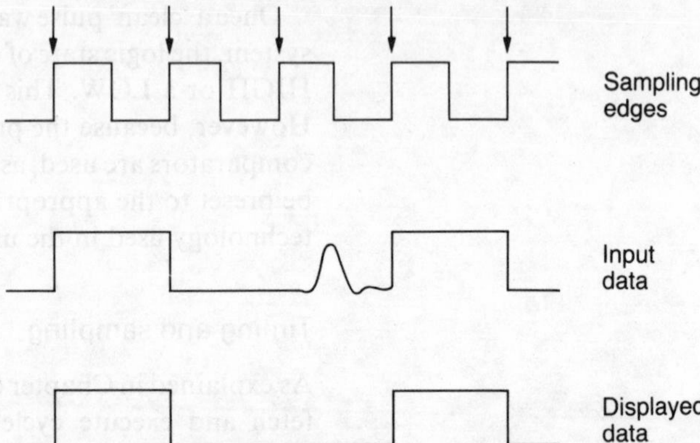

Fig. 7.7 Missing a glitch by the simple sampling method

uses an internal clock to trigger the sampling generator. The internal clock must be faster than the speed of the input data, otherwise complete logic states will go unrecorded. Generally, the practical minimum asynchronous sampling rate is four times the speed of the input data. In this way, the logic states of the input channels between clock cycles of the system under test can be investigated. Glitches can be captured provided a sampling active clock edge occurs during the glitch. This remains risky, allowing glitches to go unrecorded even with very fast internal clock speeds.

Glitches may be detected using a '*latch mode*'. The latch is normally a simple bistable circuit which is reset by the next active clock edge. The latch detects the glitch and stretches it into a single piece of data equal in length to the remaining clock period. Figure 7.8(a) shows how a latch mode represents a glitch. However glitches will still be lost if they occur at the edge of, or during, the data, as shown in (b). To overcome this, modern logic analysers include a 'full time' glitch capture circuit that captures transitions, such as glitches between sampling clocks, and stores them in a separate memory and displays them as unique characters having a coloured or bright vertical edge, to make them clearly distinguishable from the real data.

The asynchronous mode of sampling the input data suffers from an inherent inconsistency, namely that the captured data from two separate sampling sequences may differ by as much as ∓1

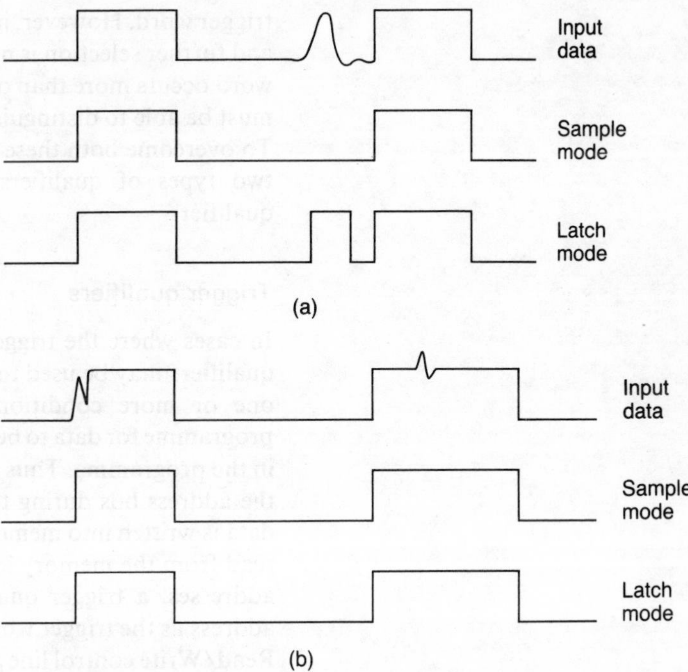

Fig. 7.8 Capturing a glitch by the latch mode method

sampling clock cycle. This is because the sampling clock is entirely independent of the input data. The active edge of the sampling clock may then occur at different times relative to the input data, as shown in 7.9.

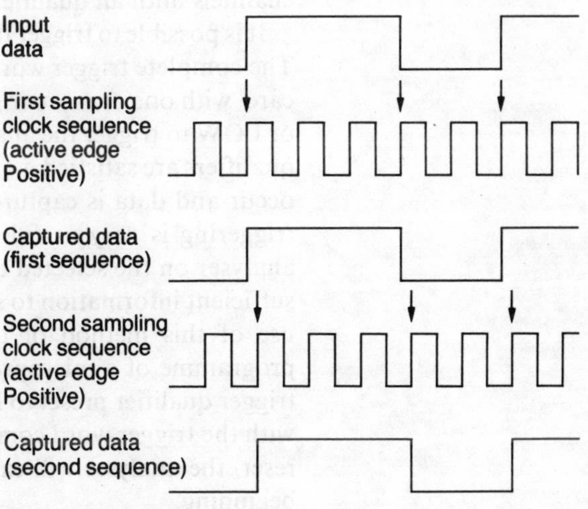

Fig. 7.9

The Qualifiers

In fault finding on a microprocessor-based system, it is essential to be able to discard irrelevant data and capture only the data surrounding the fault. By the use of a trigger word, the captured data is reduced to those occurring before and after the pre-loaded trigger word. However, in most applications, this is not sufficient, and further selection is necessary. Also, in cases where the trigger word occurs more than once in a sequence of events, the analyser must be able to distinguish and choose the required trigger event. To overcome both these problems, qualifiers are used. There are two types of qualifiers, namely trigger qualifiers and clock qualifiers.

Trigger qualifiers

In cases where the trigger word occurs more than once, trigger qualifiers may be used to define the trigger word more rigidly by one or more conditions. For example, it is common in a programme for data to be stored in a memory location for use later in the programme. Thus a particular address may occur twice on the address bus during the programme. The first time when the data is written into memory, and the second time when the data is read from the memory location. To distinguish between the two addresses, a trigger qualifier may be used. To select the first address as the trigger word, a trigger qualifier is connected to the Read/Write control line and preset to Write, e.g. LOW in the case of the 6502 microprocessor and HIGH for Z80. Conversely, to select the second time the address occurs, the trigger qualifier must be preset to Read, i.e. HIGH for the 6502 and LOW for the Z80.

Logic analysers may have as many as 40 trigger qualifiers. The analyser will neglect trigger words that appear on the input channels until all qualifiers are satisfied simultaneously.

It is possible to trigger the analyser on the trigger qualifiers only. The complete trigger word may be disabled by setting it to 'don't care' with one or more trigger qualifiers connected and set HIGH or LOW to trigger the analyser. In this case, as soon as the trigger qualifiers are satisfied, i.e. the logic states met, then triggering will occur and data is captured in the normal way. This method of triggering is very useful where it is not possible to trigger the analyser on the selected trigger word or where there may not be sufficient information to select a trigger word. An example of the use of this method of triggering is in capturing the start-up programme of a microprocessor-based system. In this case, one trigger qualifier preset to HIGH is connected to the Reset control with the trigger word completely disabled. When the processor is reset, the analyser will capture the start-up programme from its beginning.

Clock qualifiers

In cases where it is necessary to distinguish between input data and capture only that which is of interest to the user and neglect the rest, clock qualifiers may be used. Similar to the trigger qualifier, the clock qualifier may be preset to '0', '1' or 'Don't Care'. An AND function is applied to the clock qualifier and to the clock to produce a 'qualified clock', see Fig. 7.10. This enables data to be selectively recorded. With the clock qualifier set to 'X' (don't

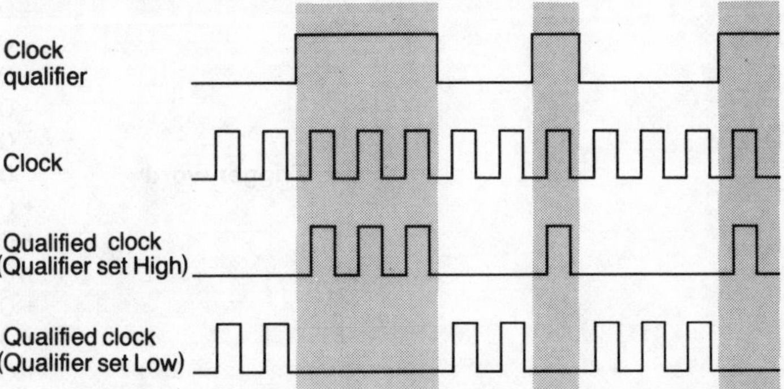

Fig. 7.10 The clock qualifier

care), the analyser will capture and record data at every active clock edge. With the qualifier set to '1' or '0' the analyser records data at the active edge of the appropriate qualified clock. For example, consider the displayed data shown in Table 7.2. The selected trigger word is 003402 and the sequence of events occurring on the address and data buses is as shown. If a fault, e.g. a glitch, is suspected to occur when the microprocessor is reading from memory, then for fault finding purposes only the sequence of events when the Read control line is active are of interest. A clock qualifier may then be used to disregard all inputs except those occurring during Read operations. The qualifier is connected to the appropriate control line which in the case of a 6502 microprocessor being used, is the R/$\overline{W}$ (Read/Not Write) line. This means that the control line is at logic '1' when a Read operation is executed and at logic '0' when a Write operation is executed. The qualifier is therefore set to '1' for Read. With the trigger word set to 003402 as before, the analyser will only capture data when the microprocessor is Reading, namely the data shown in Table 7.3. It can be seen that 021BAA and 021CFF have been disregarded by the analyser as these are not Read operations. Conversely, if a fault was suspected during a Write operation, the clock qualifier should be set to logic '0' to capture the events when the microprocessor is writing into memory. In this case, the trigger word must be changed since 003402 does not occur during a Write operation. Either 021BAA or 021CFF may be chosen. Assuming the trigger word is set to 021BAA and the qualifier to '0', the analyser will then capture the data shown in Table 7.4.

As far as triggering is concerned, the qualifier acts in the same way as any input channel, and as such may be considered as a part of the trigger word to be recognized by the analyser. However, unlike the input channels, the data on a qualifier is not captured by the analyser, and therefore is not displayed.

Table 7.3

	Cursor Count	*Data displayed (HEX)*
	– 05	Random
	– 04	0030 A9
	– 03	0031 AA
	– 02	0032 8D
	– 01	0033 1B
Trigger word	**00**	**0034 02**
	+ 01	0035 A9
	+ 02	0036 FF
	+ 03	0037 8D
	+ 04	0038 IC
	+ 05	0039 02
	+ 06	003A 00
	+ 07	Random

Table 7.4

	Cursor Count	*Data*
	– 01	Random
Trigger word	**00**	**021B AA**
	+ 01	021C FF
	+ 02	Random

Analysers may have any number between 2 and 40 qualifiers, which are connected to the analyser via a probe pod. A complete block diagram for a logic analyser is shown in Fig. 7.11.

Other triggering techniques

The trigger word, trigger and clock qualification, give a basic method of triggering the logic analyser. In most cases, further techniques in the selection and acquisition of data is necessary. *Delay* may be added to the trigger event, as shown in Fig. 7.12. When delay is used, the analyser waits for a specific number of clock cycles after the triggering event before it begins to capture the data. The number of delay cycles is pre-loaded into the analyser by the user. Some analysers can delay the capture of data until the trigger event recurs a specified number of times.

Further definition of the trigger event may be achieved by using *multiple-word triggering*. In this, more than one trigger word is used, all of which must be satisfied before the analyser begins to capture the data.

Triggering may depend on a sequence of events, e.g. a part of a programme which when it occurs triggers the analyser. This is known as *sequential-event triggering*.

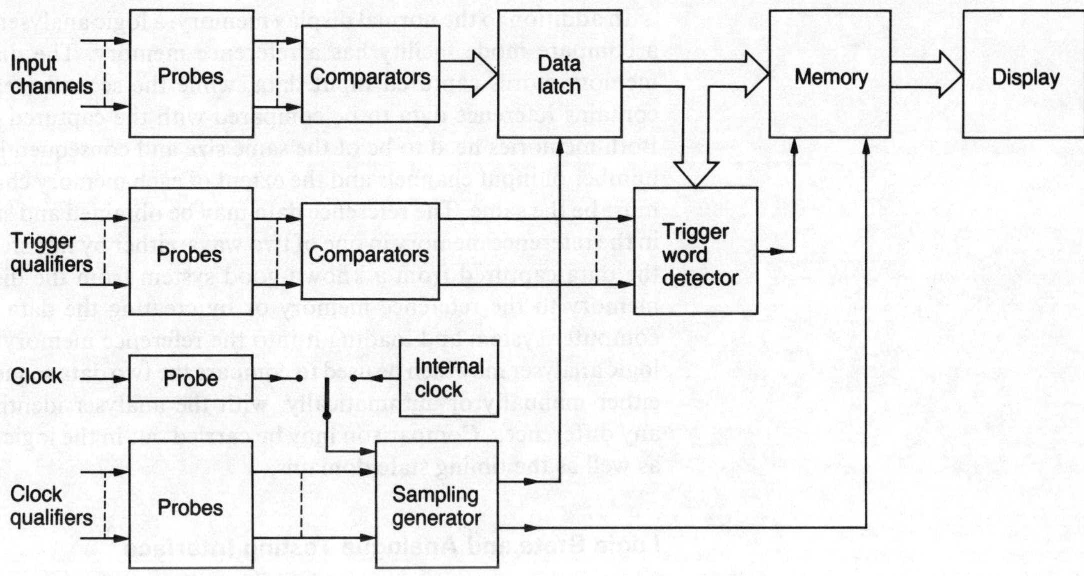

Fig. 7.11 The complete block diagram for a logic analyser

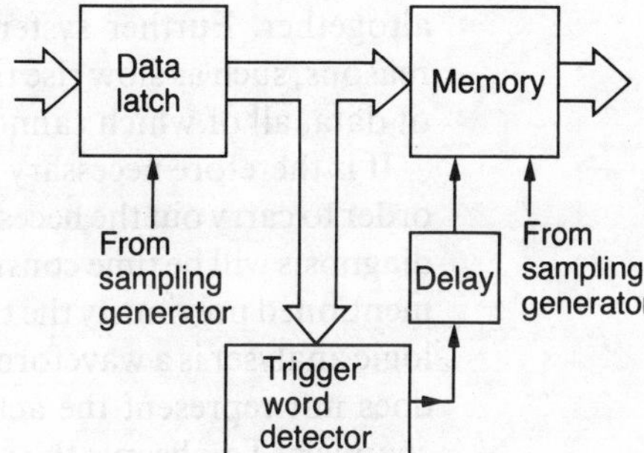

Fig. 7.12 Delayed triggering technique

Finally, the analyser may be triggered on the non-occurrence of a word, a multiple word, or a sequential event, as well as on their occurrence. In this way, the analyser may be made to capture data only when a certain event fails to occur, i.e. when a fault occurs.

Compare mode

The basic function of a logic analyser is to capture a selected sequence of data occurring in a system under test. This data may then be displayed for examination by a technician to verify the workings of the system and to identify a fault. Verification or fault-finding implies a previous knowledge of the system, and of some expected sequence of data. Verification and fault-finding thus consists of a comparison between what is captured and what is expected. To facilitate this activity, a compare mode is incorporated in modern logic analysers.

In addition to the normal display memory, a logic analyser with a compare mode facility has a reference memory. The display memory stores captured input data, while the second memory contains reference data to be compared with the captured data. Both memories need to be of the same size and consequently the number of input channels and the extent of each memory channel must be the same. The reference data may be obtained and stored in the reference memory in one of two ways: either by transferring the data captured from a known-good system from the display memory to the reference memory or by creating the data on a computer system and loading it into the reference memory. The logic analyser may then be used to compare the two data sequences either manually or automatically, with the analyser identifying any differences. Comparison may be carried out in the logic state as well as the timing state domains.

Logic State and Analogue Testing Interface

Fault-finding does not end with capturing and identifying the responsible glitch. In fact, it is only the beginning of the process to rectify the fault by reducing the glitch amplitude or removing it altogether. Further system malfunction may occur for various reasons, such as slow rise time, low amplitude, or wrong hold time of data, all of which cannot be identified by a logic state display.

It is therefore necessary to observe the actual data waveform in order to carry out the necessary measurements without which fault diagnosis will be time consuming and solutions difficult to find. As mentioned previously the time waveform analysis produced by the logic analyser is a waveform representation of the captured data. It does not represent the actual waveforms occurring at the input channels. To observe the actual time waveforms we have to cross over to analogue measurements using an oscilloscope. Figure 7.13 shows a logic state timing diagram produced by a logic analyser

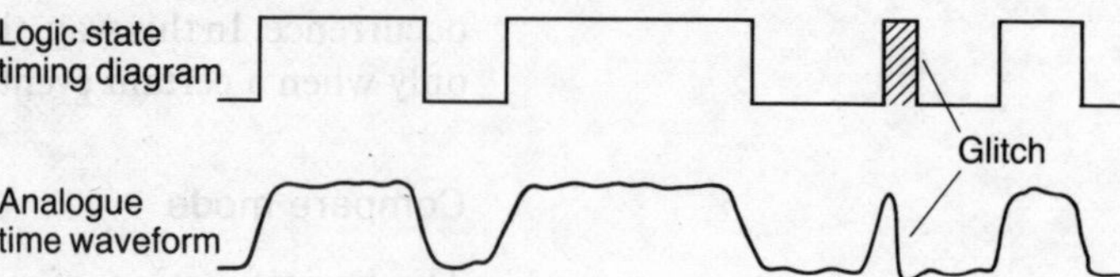

Fig. 7.13

and the actual analogue time waveform as captured by a storage oscilloscope. Measurements to verify amplitude, rise time, hold time and relative timing with other waveforms, as well as to investigate glitches, can be made on the analogue time waveforms. Oscilloscopes used for the purpose of capturing data waveforms are of the digitizing storage type, with advanced triggering facilities similar to those used in logic analysers. In the area of overlap between the oscilloscope and the logic analyser, a combined test device is the obvious answer, whereby the data captured by the logic analyser is also captured by the storage oscilloscope and may be displayed simultaneously.

Signature Analysers

Logic analysis is employed mainly in design and development, although programmable logic analysers may be used in production testing as part of an automatic test system (ATS).

In fault-finding, logic analysers suffer from the need to interpret the captured data, which means a prior knowledge of the workings of the circuit. Skilled manpower is, therefore, necessary. The signature analyser is designed to overcome this problem by allowing unskilled labour to diagnose and repair most faults in a system.

Principle of signature analysis

The introduction of digital electronics rendered the concept of signal tracing impractical as a method for fault diagnosis. In analogue electronics, an immediately recognizable waveform with specified frequency and amplitude is present at each test point as shown in Fig. 7.14. By comparing actual waveforms present on a system with those expected on a good system, the test engineer can identify a fault. In digital electronics, this procedure is not possible since trains of pulses representing binary codes look very similar to each other. The equivalent of an analogue waveform at a test point is a compression of a stream of bit pulses at a node into a recognizable word such as a hexadecimal number, known as a 'signature'.

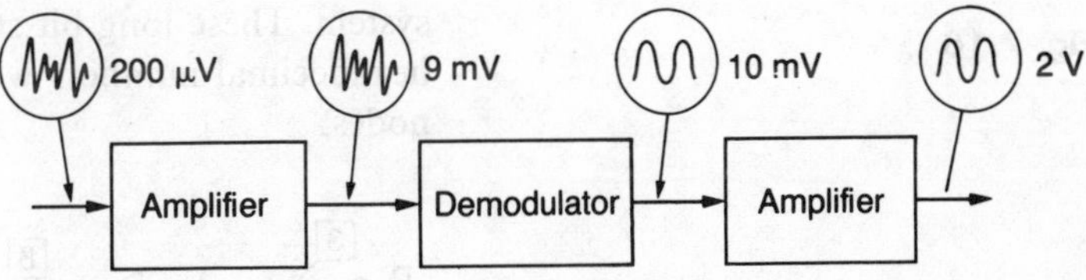

Fig. 7.14 Analogue schematic with expected waveforms at various test points

Consider a simple gate combination as shown in Fig. 7.15. D_0 and D_1 are the input data and P_0 and P_1 the output data. The truth table is as shown in Table 7.5. One method of testing the function of the gate combination is to go through its truth table. The waveforms occurring at the inputs and outputs when the test programme is run are as shown in Fig. 7.16. With an input of 0011 at D_0 and 0101 at D_1 the outputs are P_0: 0111 and P_1: 1010. These streams of binary bits may be considered as the 'digital waveforms' or signatures at the inputs and outputs. For simplicity, the

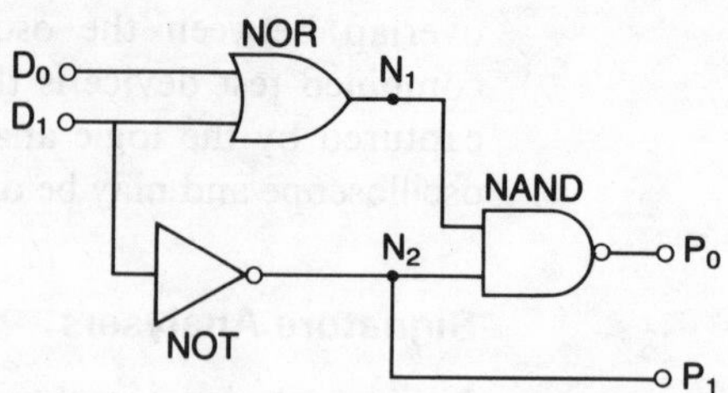

Fig. 7.15

Table 7.5

D_0	D_1	*Node* N_1	*Node* N_2	P_0	P_1
0	0	1	1	0	1
0	1	0	0	1	0
1	0	0	1	1	1
1	1	0	0	1	0

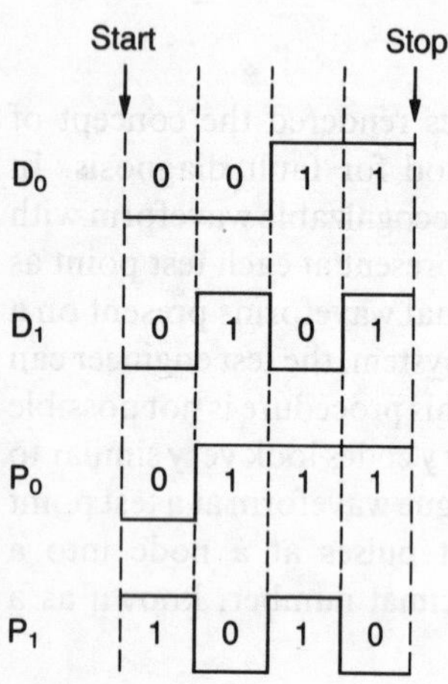

Fig. 7.16

signatures are compressed into a convenient form such as hexadecimal numbers. In our example, the output signatures will thus be P_0: 7 (HEX) and P_1: A (HEX). Similarly, for any other nodes, such as N_1 and N_2 the signatures are 1000 = 8 (HEX) and 1010 = A (HEX) respectively. This is the principle of signature analysis, namely the compression of a data stream at a test node into a unique simple signature. Fault diagnosis may thus be reduced to feeding in the appropriate input data and testing for the appropriate signatures at the primary outputs and other test nodes. In place of the waveforms displayed on an analogue circuit diagram to assist in fault diagnosis, a digital circuit diagram may display signatures at the various nodes, as shown in Fig. 7.17. For complex digital circuitry, especially microprocessor-based systems, longer bit streams at the inputs are necessary to fully test the system. These long bit streams are then compressed into 4-digit hexadecimal numbers which represent the signatures at the test nodes.

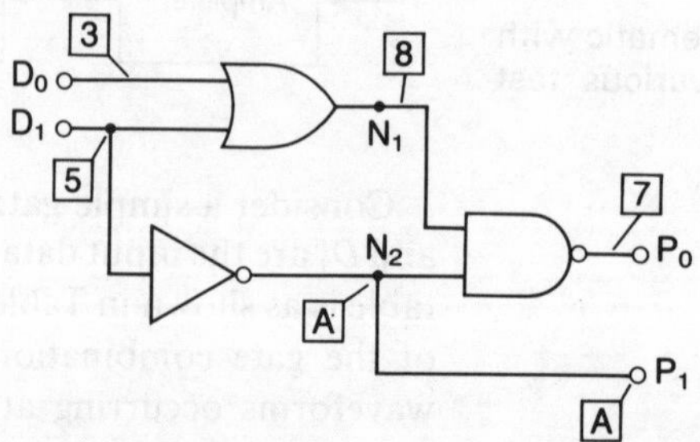

Fig. 7.17 Digital schematic with expected signature at various nodes

The simplest type of signature analyser is that shown in Fig. 7.18. The start signal begins the process of capturing the data bits in the shift register. This process is terminated by a stop signal into

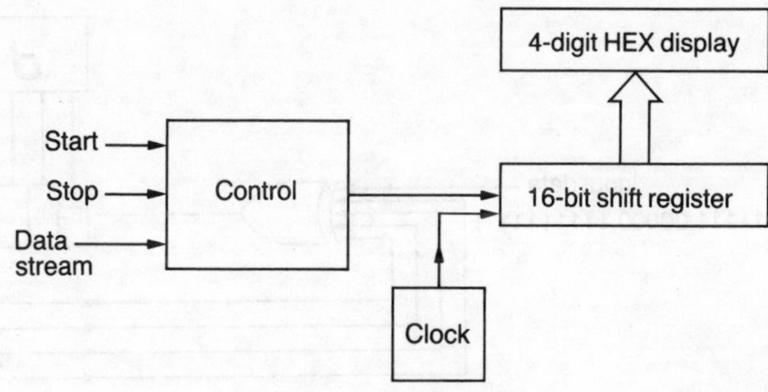

Fig. 7.18 Basic principles of a signature analysis

the control. The data bits captured by the shift register are then displayed as a 4-digit HEX signature. As may be seen in Fig. 7.19, with the control signals 'start' and 'stop' as indicated, the data

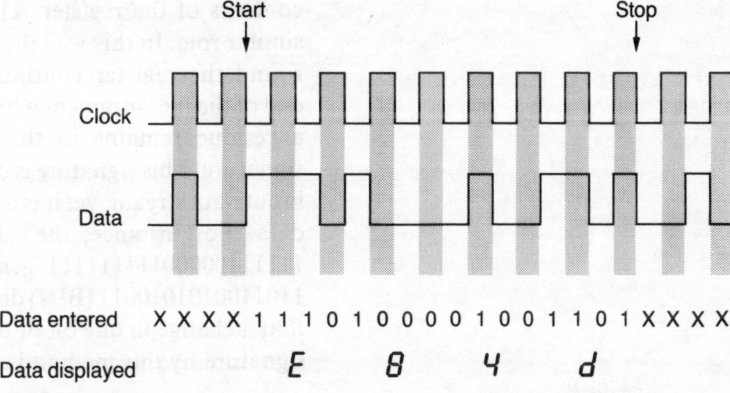

Fig. 7.19 Timing diagram for a signature analysis

captured by the signature analyser is as shown. The shift register transfers the bits from left to right at the selected edge of the clock waveform (negative edges in this case). Thus following the start trigger edge, the shift register begins to sample and capture the data bits at every negative clock edge. This continues until the gate is closed by a 'stop' trigger edge. The data entered and displayed is therefore 1110100001001101 = E84D (HEX). This simple signature analyser suffers from an obvious disadvantage, namely it cannot handle a data stream longer than 16 bits. After the 16th bit, data bits will begin to be lost with only the last 16 remaining in the register to be displayed. This may be overcome by expanding the shift register to 24, 32, 64, ..., bits which produces signatures of 6, 8, 16 ... hexadecimal digits. Such a method is impractical and, even for a 64-bit data input, is expensive. A clever way of overcoming this limitation is the use of **Cyclic Redundancy Count,** employing four feedback loops in the shift register. This ensures that data bits longer than 16 are recirculated producing a unique signature of 4 digits only, see Fig. 7.20. The feedback loops are connected to the input of the register via the exclusive-OR gate shown. The register is reset to zero before the input data is fed into it. Up to the

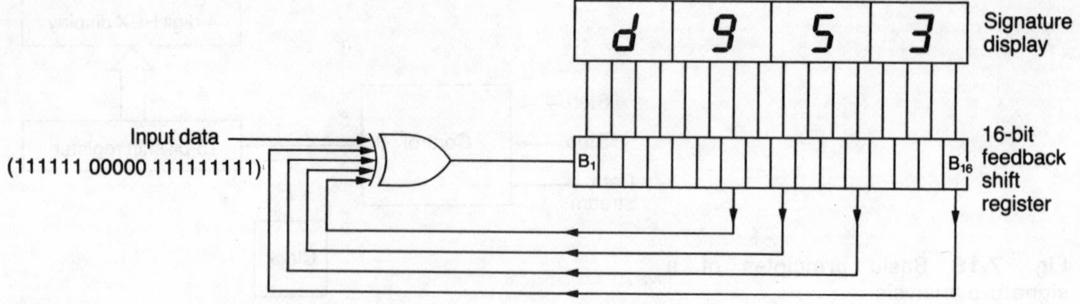

Fig. 7.20 Basic block diagram for a signature analyser

seventh input bit, the register acts as a shift register. At the seventh bit, the first feedback loop comes into operation, which affects the contents of the register. The other three feedback loops play a similar role. In this way the bits are not lost but merely circulated round the register continuously updating its contents. At the end of the measurement when the stop trigger edge closes the gate, a residue remains in the register which is displayed as the signature. This signature is completely dissimilar from the original input data stream, yet it is a unique representation of that original data. For instance, the 20-bit input sequence in Fig. 7.20 of 11111100000111111111 generates a unique 16-bit signature of 1101100101010011 (BIN) displayed as D953 (HEX). The certainty that a change in one bit of the input data will generate a different signature by this method is 99.998%.

Signature-analyser block diagram

Figure 7.21 shows a block diagram for a signature analyser using the feedback shift register described earlier. The control unit ensures that only the selected data bits are entered into the register. The start and stop opens and closes the 'measurement window' during which input data bits may be entered into the shift register. The clock input is a sampling pulse which is used to select the

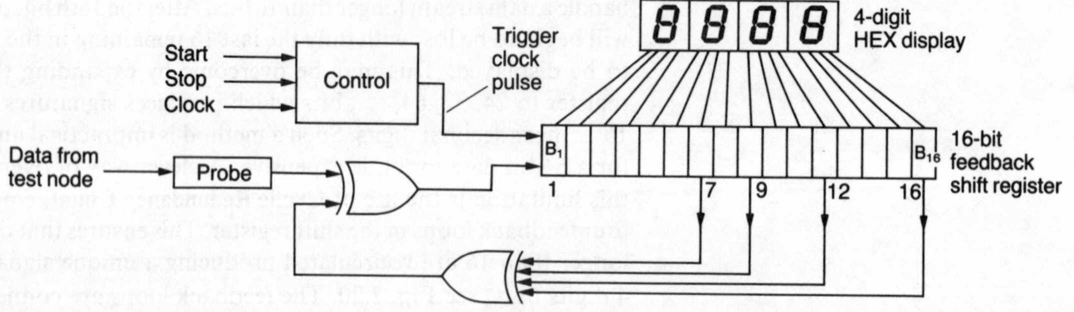

Fig. 7.21 Signature analyser block diagram

required bits from the input data streams. Sometimes it is connected to the timing clock of the unit under test to allow every bit of the input data to be entered into the register. Alternatively, it may be connected to another control, e.g. the Read or Write lines, in which case only the data bits associated with a Read or a Write sequence are entered. The ouput of the control unit is used as the common clock pulse for the 16-bit shift register. The input data is fed into the EX-OR gate via a probe before going into the shift register. When the data is entered into the shift register and modified by the feedback loops, it is then displayed as a unique signature of that particular input data stream.

The use of the signature analyser

As mentioned earlier, the signature analyser opens the way for technicians to test and repair a digital system without detailed knowledge of the circuit. In order to do this, test programmes must be written to test the various parts of the system. The system is then stimulated with the test programme and a signature analyser is used to test for correct signatures at pre-determined test nodes. The test programme may be stored in ROM in the system under test itself, or it may be fed in externally by a peripheral device or by the signature analyser itself. The signature at each node is monitored and compared with that produced by a known-good system. The analyser may have a facility to store the known-good signatures to make immediate comparisons. Any incorrect signature indicates a fault. This fault may be identified by 'signature tracing' which involves testing other nodes to identify the faulty block.

As an example, consider the simplified Z80 microprocessor-based system shown in Fig. 7.22. It is intended to test memory chip ROM 1. First, a stimulus programme is written which reads all locations in ROM 1 in sequence from 0000 to 07FF. The contents of each location will thus be placed on the data bus in sequence. The programme may be applied to the system externally or be stored in ROM 2. Before the first location in ROM 1 is read, the programme sets the start trigger edge of the signature analyser to open its gate. When all the locations have been read, the programme then sets the stop trigger edge to close the gate. The input probe of the signature analyser is connected to data bus line D_0 to capture the data stream and generate a signature for that data line. To ensure that only the contents of ROM 1 locations are entered into the signature analyser, a clock signal must be chosen that will trigger only when ROM 1 is set at Read, that is ROM 1 chip select CS1. The Read RD control line may also be used as a clock. However, in this case, all data from other memory chips which the microprocessor may fetch in the execution of the stimulus programme (from ROM 2 for instance) will also be

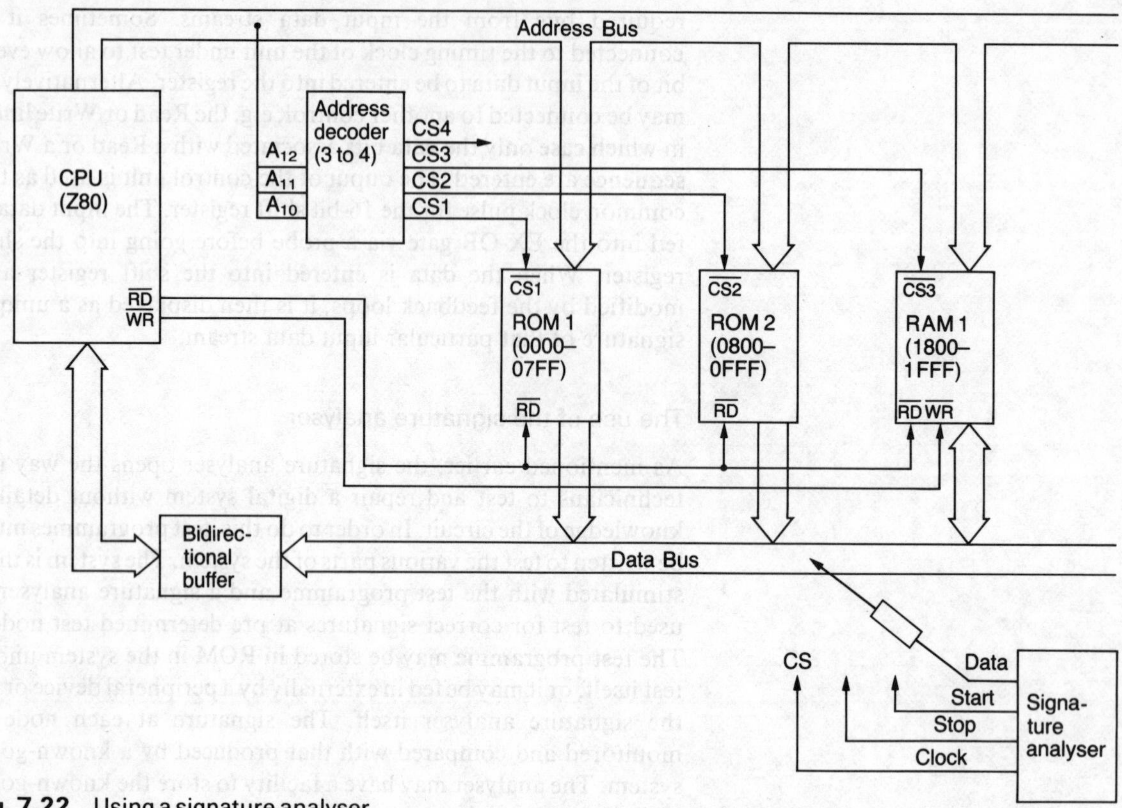

Fig. 7.22 Using a signature analyser to test a microprocessor based system

entered into the signature analyser. This is acceptable provided such data are known to be good. When the signature for data bus line D_0 is verified, the test is repeated for D_1, D_2 and so on up to D_7. These signatures are compared with those generated by a known-good system to verify chip ROM 1.

A similar testing process may be carried out for ROM 2 and RAM 1.

8 Microprocessor-based instruments

Until recently, programmability in an instrument meant the ability to digitally select the function and range of a counter or a multimeter or to select the ouput parameter of a signal generator. Programmable instruments have the ability to memorize a set up sequence or a test programme. Today, with the use of microprocessors, programmable instruments have become complete testing systems as opposed to mere measuring instruments. Not only every parameter of an instrument is made programmable, but such instruments, with the use of a standard bus connector, are amenable to control by an external controller. Programmable instruments have created a revolution in product testing and fault-finding, linking together what has been previously treated as separate parts of testing into a whole system.

The use of microprocessors provides data processing capabilities such as carrying out mathematic calculation and computations, making comparisons and producing statistical information. This is over and above the normal programming capabilities, such as setting the range, function, output levels and frequences. For this reason, programmable microprocessor-based instruments are known as *'intelligent'* instruments.

A general basic block diagram for a microprocessor-based test instrument is shown in Fig. 8.1. As can be seen, it is very similar to other microprocessor-based systems as described in Chapter 6.

A programme is entered into the system via the keyboard and is stored in RAM. The ROM contains the setting-up initializing and sub-routine programmes. When the programme is run, the CPU (the microprocessor) instructs the A-to-D converter to take a sample of the analogue input, convert it into an 8-bit parallel digital word and place it on to the data bus. The CPU receives this data and processes it as instructed by the programme. It may display the result on the VDU, store it in RAM for future reference, or compare it with a reference store in RAM. The process is then repeated by an instruction to the A-to-D converter to take another sample. The sampling or reading rate is determined by the programme and may vary from one reading every hour to hundreds every second.

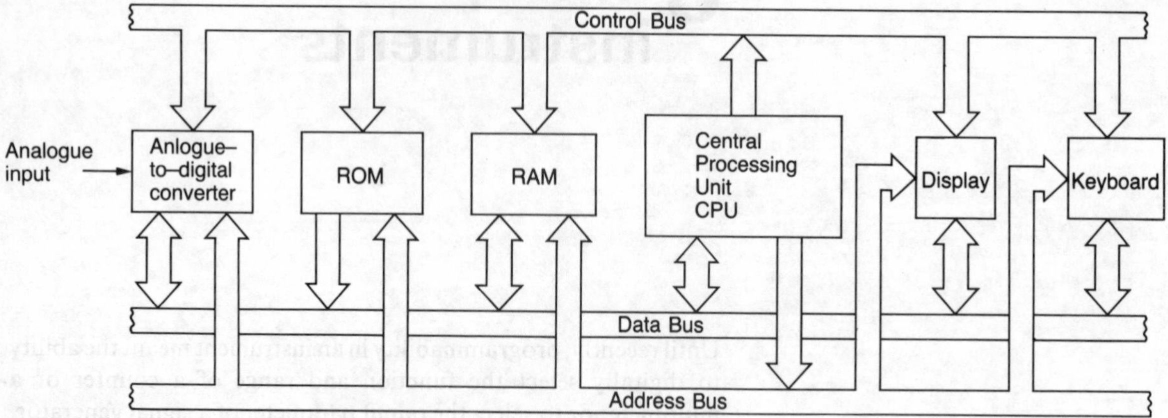

Fig. 8.1 General block diagram for a microprocessor-based instrument

The instrument may also be used for data processing, such as computing maximum and minimum readings over a period of time, percentages and statistical information such as averages, variance or standard deviation. Other peripheral devices such as a printer may be added to the instrument via a suitable interface connector. A number of such instruments may be used under a common controller or computer to build an automatic test system.

Features of some Microprocessor-based Instruments

Microprocessor-based DMMs

The microprocessor-based DMM has the following features:

1. variable reading rate;
2. memory store to capture hundreds of separate readings;
3. data processing facilities where each reading may be manipulated according to a mathematical formula;
4. ability to produce statistical information;
5. ability to compute readings into dBs;
6. automatic calibration
7. self-test facility which may be initiated on power-up condition.

The oscilloscope

A microprocessor-based oscilloscope is a digitizing storage oscilloscope controlled by a microprocessor. Following a high rate of digitizing, the waveform is stored in RAM to be manipulated and processed by the microprocessor. The waveform may be expanded for detailed examination, stored for future reference, compared with other stored or captured waveforms, or analysed by the microprocessor. The microprocessor may also be used to carry out automatic measurements on the waveform properties such as amplitude, rms and peak-to-peak voltages, d.c. level, period, rise time, over-shoot, under-shoot, frequency, phase shift and so on. Such measurements are made by the use of voltage and time cursors (see Fig. 8.2). The operator simply sets the voltage cursors at the appropriate points of the waveform and the microprocessor will compute the voltage difference. Similarly with the time cursors.

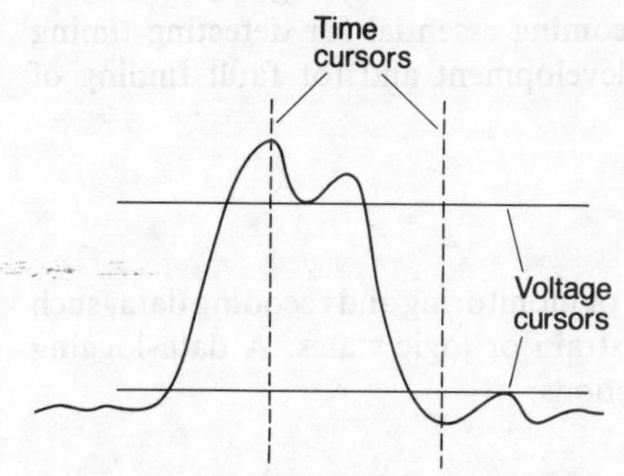

Fig. 8.2 Oscilloscope display with time and voltage cursors

Measurement read-outs, as well as a listing of the CRO setting and other information, are displayed on the CRT itself by the microprocessor. A typical display for a single channel is shown in Fig. 8.3. Microprocessor-based CROs allow programmed testing to be repeated and stored for examination. This is particularly useful in life testing of products and in measuring the worst cases of rise time of pulses, hold-up time and voltage level of pulse trains. The microprocessor captures the information repeatedly over a period of time, and gives the maximum and minimum values as well as the scatter, percentage variation and other statistical information.

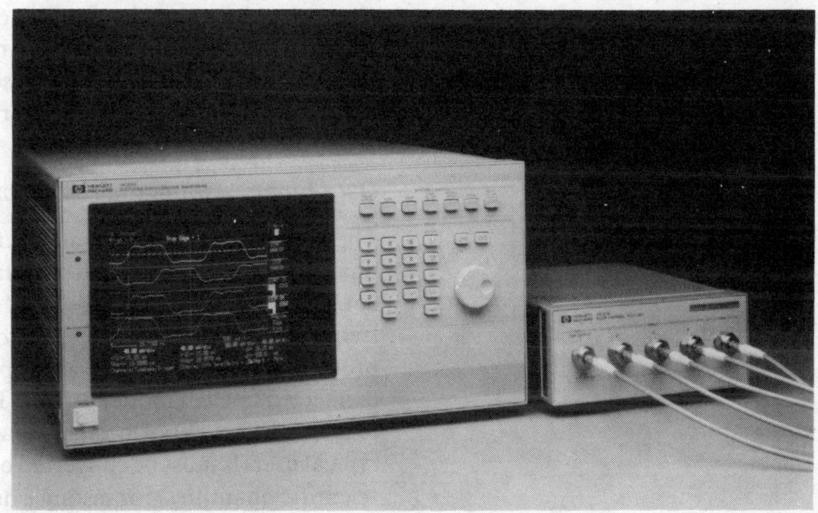

Fig. 8.3 A typical display of a microprocessor-based oscilloscope showing four simultaneous beams (Courtesy Hewlett Packard Ltd.)

More sophisticated triggering is possible with this type of oscilloscope, especially when used to test microprocessor-based units. Multiple trigger input channels, often 30 or more, are used to achieve what is known as '*state trigger*' or '*parallel word trigger*'. This method of triggering is similar to that used in a digital analyser, where the logic state of each trigger input channel is preset to HIGH or LOW. When that condition is recognized by the oscilloscope, it captures and displays the waveform. Triggering may be delayed in time or events or qualified by the setting of a cursor. Recent oscilloscopes have a facility for triggering on a missing bit or an extra bit (e.g. a glitch) in a serial data stream. With multiple inputs and state triggering facility, the microprocessor-based oscilloscope provides a bridge between the purely analogue oscilloscope on the one hand, and the logic state analyser on the other, which is becoming essential for detecting timing problems in design and development and for fault finding of microprocessor systems.

Data Logging Systems

Data logging is the process of monitoring and recoding data, such as temperature, pressure, strain or logic states. A data logging system has three basic functions:

1. data acquisition;
2. data manipulation and reduction;
3. data logging.

Data acquisition

Simple data logging systems acquire data from just a few input channels. More complex systems can receive data from hundreds or even thousands of input channels. The input channels are scanned sequentially in the case of few input channels, or according to a preset sequence for a more complex system.

Data manipulation and reduction

The measurements to be made by the logging system are physical quantities such as temperature, strain or pressure. They must be converted into electrical data such as voltage, current or frequency, before they are fed into the data logging system. This process is carried out by an appropriate transducer or sensor connected to each input channel. The data that is acquired by the logger is what is known as 'raw data' which means very little to a typical user. It must be converted or reduced to more recognizable scientific quantities, for instance degrees Celsius for temperature. Further data manipulations are normally separately carried out on the acquired data from each input channel, as well as on the data from different channels. Such data manipulation includes determining averages, maximum and minimum values, standard deviation, comparisons and other mathematical analysis and conclusions.

Data logging

Once the data has been acquired and manipulated, the results are then produced on a print-out or a display. The data may be logged into a memory, a cassette or a disc.

Figure 8.4 shows a basic logging system. The logging system

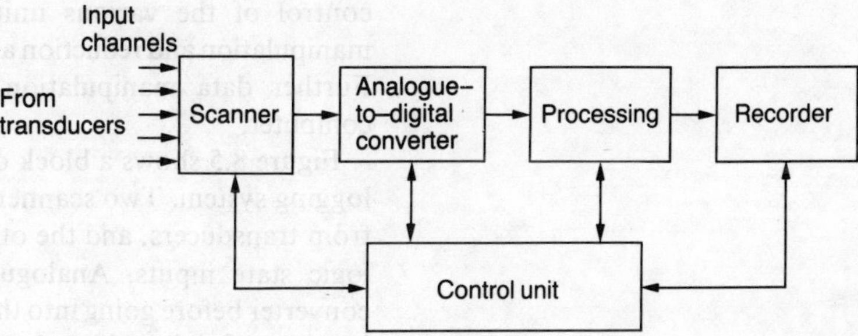

Fig. 8.4 Data logging system

makes a large number of measurements accurately and rapidly. The quantities to be measured are first converted to electrical quantities by a transducer or sensor, before being fed into the scanner. The logger monitors each input channel separately, allowing enough time for the measurement to be completed before switching to the next channel. The switching is carried out by the scanner which, by using reed relays, connects each channel in turn to the logger. The analogue signals fed into the logger are converted into a digital code by the A-to-D converter. The convertor is normally a digital voltmeter or multimeter where the transducer device produces a varying direct or alternating voltage. Where the transducer produces a varying frequency, the convertor used is a frequency counter.

Because the data is in digital form, the logger can manipulate and process the readings without any loss of accuracy or sensitivity. Simple data manipulations are carried out by the processing unit.

An example of the use of a logging system is in monitoring the temperature at various points of a refrigerator or an oven. The logger could periodically sample temperatures at various points, keep track of maximum and minimum values and sound an alarm if any point deviates from the average temperature by more than a certain preset value. The data logger could also report daily on the standard deviation from the mean, maximum and minimum values of each temperature point and can also indicate trends. The recorder may be a print-out, an instrument recorder, a display device, a cassette or a disc. The system is controlled by the control unit which determines the scanning rate, the type of conversion and the processing requirements. It also initiates the recording process and generally ensures the system runs in synchronism.

Many transducers, such as a thermocouple, suffer from non-linearity, which must be corrected to produce accurate readings. This is carried out by what is known as a 'linearizer', which compensates for the non-linear characteristics of the transducer to produce a linear response. Some transducers give an output when the quantity being sensed is zero. In these transducers, an offset to compensate for non-zero output is often provided.

Modern data loggers are microprocessor based, where the

control of the various units, the timing and extensive data manipulation and reduction are carried out by the microprocessor. Further data manipulation is often carried out by external computer.

Figure 8.5 shows a block diagram for a microprocessor-based logging system. Two scanners are used: one for analogue inputs from transducers, and the other a digital scanner for digital and logic state inputs. Analogue inputs are fed into the A-to-D converter before going into the microprocessor controller. Digital inputs are fed directly to the microprocessor. The microprocessor carries out the control function as well as that of data manipulation and reduction. Very complex data manipulation may be carried out by a peripheral computer via the IEEE-488 bus interface connector (see Chapter 10).

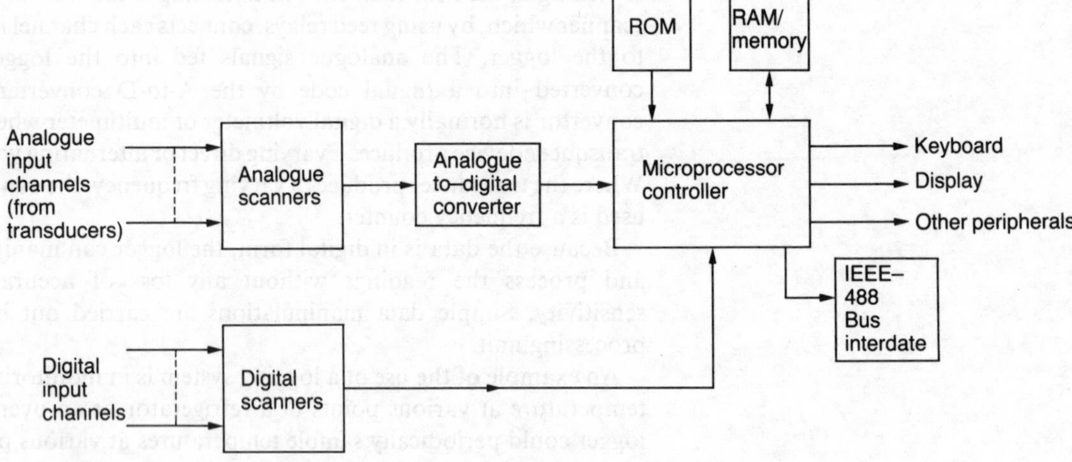

Fig. 8.5 Microprocessor-based data logging system

A microprocessor-based logging system has the following features:

1. Multiple programmable analogue and digital inputs.
2. Multiple input ranges.
3. Multiple linearization for each input channel.
4. Programmable alarm system.
5. Status digital inputs, such as the logic state of switches or other test points in a system.
6. Event digital inputs where the logger continuously looks for events to occur. When the specified event, e.g. a logic level, occurs at the input, the microprocessor is interrupted and a programmed task is carried out.
7. Normal processing such as unit conversion.

8. Data manipulation and reduction, such as calculating averages etc., as well as mathematical analysis of multi-channel data.
9. Standard bus interface (IEEE 488) for direct connection to extra computing capabilities and other peripherals.
10. Background mode of operation. Where a microprocessor has to scan and sample a large number of input channels very rapidly, data manipulation takes a comparatively long time, thus limiting the rate of scanning. To overcome this, computation tasks and analysis are carried out in the 'background' simultaneously with continuously monitoring and reading the input channels.
11. Stimulus capabilities. Output channels are provided which may be used to stimulate external equipment through a defined sequence of operations. For example, a task of observing the temperature at one point can cause a second task to start when the observed temperature crosses a pre-defined threshold level. The second task may be monitoring temperature at other points, sounding an alarm or stimulating the system into a controlled operation.

9 Automatic testing

In any test system, a number of instruments are employed (a) to stimulate the unit under test (UUT) and (b) to make measurements of the responses.

Figure 9.1 shows the basic principles of a test system. A stimulus device, such as a signal generator, is set to feed an appropriate test signal into the UUT. A measuring device, such as a DVM, is set to make measurements and produce readings of the responses of the UUT. The result of the test is then compared with standard results, i.e. those expected from a known-good unit, and conclusions made. In a manual test system, the test facilities are utilized by separate human action to select, connect and control the test instruments, to observe, record and compare the measurements made and to evaluate the test data. In an automatic test system, the human activity is carried out automatically (either wholly or in part) by a test programme.

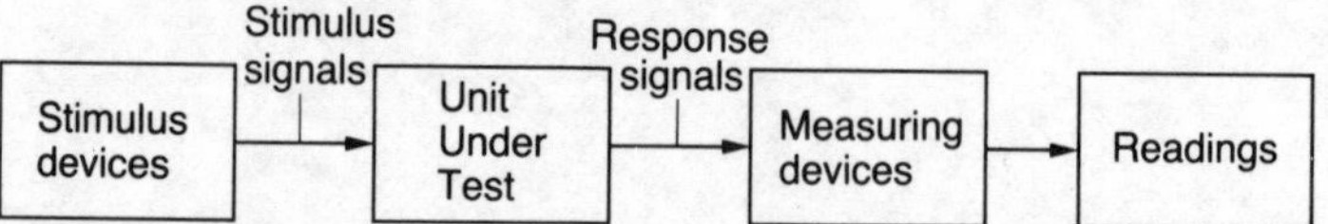

Fig. 9.1 Basic principles of a test system

Requirements for a Test System

A test system, whether testing active or passive components, printed circuit boards, equipment, or complete systems, must have the following items:

1. Stimulus test devices to provide the appropriate input signal to the UUT. They include d.c. supplies to provide power to the UUT as well as signal generators for sinusoidal input, pulse generators for digital circuitry, and other devices to provide input data for bus structured UUTs.
2. Measuring devices to make the necessary measurements of the output responses produced by the UUT. They include DMMs to measure voltage levels and resistance; oscilloscopes to monitor such things as waveshapes, risetime and phase shifts; frequency meters and logic analysers.

3. Switching arrangements to ensure that the appropriate stimulus and measuring devices are connected to the appropriate input or output terminals respectively.
4. Facility to control the stimulus and measuring test devices. This includes such things as setting the range, frequency, amplitude, pulse width and trigger words.
5. Ability to compare test results with expected (standard) results and make decisions. This includes such things as pass/fail indication, diagnosis of faulty components and further tests.
6. Interface facility, to make connection to the UUT. This interface may be an edge connector, individual clips to test points, or a more complex fixture such as a 'bed of nails', making contact with hundreds of test points.

Basic Block Diagram

An automatic tester must meet the basic requirements described above. A basic block diagram is shown in Fig. 9.2. The UUT is connected to the tester via an interface or an adaptor which connects the various test points on the UUT to the test system. The UUT receives test stimulus signals and sends output response signals to the tester via the interface.

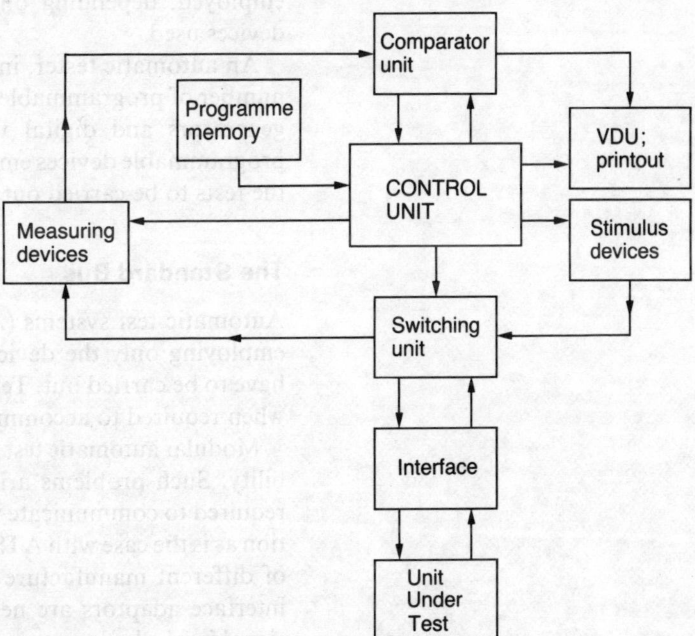

Fig. 9.2 Basic block diagram for an automatic tester

The control unit runs a sequence of tests in accordance with a test programme. For each test the switching unit is used to connect selected test signals from the stimulus unit to the appropriate test points, and simultaneously connects selected measuring devices to the appropriate test points. The test is then initiated, the measurements are made, and the readings are recorded. When one test is completed, the control unit then initiates the next test in the sequence. The switching unit consists of a matrix of a large number of switches normally of the reed relay type. The switches are also controlled by the control unit, which is able to use some or all the switches and set them in any combination to be used as a signal path to and from the tester.

For each test, the control unit selects the type and specification of stimulus signal required, such as a 1-kHz 10-mV sinewave or a 1-MHz 5-V pulse. It also selects the appropriate measuring devices required for the particular test. The readings from the measuring devices are then compared with standard pre-programmed readings obtained when testing a known-good unit. The results of this comparison and the conclusions drawn, such as pass or fail or faulty IC, together with the actual readings, are produced on an output peripheral device such as a printer or a VDU.

Automatic testing may be used for a variety of units: digital or analogue, audio, radio or very high frequencies or bus-structured devices. The difference between one application and another is the type of stimulus devices and measuring devices used. For analogue applications A-to-D and D-to-A converters may have to be employed, depending on the type of stimulus and measuring devices used.

An automatic tester, in essence, consists of a controller and a number of programmable devices, such as switching units, signal generators and digital voltmeters. The number and type of programmable devices employed depends on the type of UUT and the tests to be carried out on that UUT.

The Standard Bus

Automatic test systems (ATS) may be built on a modular basis employing only the devices necessary for the specific tests that have to be carried out. Test systems can thus be expanded as and when required to accommodate other test requirements.

Modular automatic test systems introduce problems of compatibility. Such problems arise when a number of instruments are required to communicate with one another in a system configuration as is the case with ATS. This is especially so when instruments of different manufacture are used in a system. Many different interface adaptors are needed to cope with the wide variety of signal levels, logic conversions, codes, formats and so on, that are in use throughout the world.

To overcome these problems, a standard instrument interface bus has been adopted which allows the various parts of a test system to be connected together without the need for special adaptors. The standard bus structure provides a complete bidirectional communication between the individual units of the test system. There are two types of buses: the parallel bus and the serial bus.

The parallel bus uses separate wires to interconnect each bus line. In other words, one wire must be allocated for each data, address and control line. The serial bus, on the other hand, uses only two lines to transfer the information from one system to another. Parallel information at one end must therefore be converted to serial data before being transmitted along a serial bus connector. Parallel buses are used for short distances (about 2 m or less), while serial buses are used for long distance communications, e.g. computer to terminal. The most popular bus interfaces in use in instrumentation are the RS 232 series bus, and the general purpose interface bus.

The General Purpose Interface Bus (GPIB)

This is the most commonly used parallel interface bus in testing and instrumentation. The GPIB is also known as the IEEE-488 bus. It employs a 24-pin connector, of which 16 are assigned to specific signals and the remaining 8 are ground and shields. The 16 signal lines are normally divided into 8 bidirectional data lines and 8 control lines. The control lines may include such controls as data valid, service request and no data accepted. The standard specification defines the function assigned to each pin together with the voltage and current values necessary for data transfer. Instruments with IEEE-488 parallel bus interface option may be connected together merely by plugging the appropriate connector cable, as shown in Fig. 9.3 between the various instruments. Instrument A is a stimulus device which 'listens', i.e. receives instructions via the bus. Instrument B is a measuring device which 'listens' and 'talks', i.e. receives instructions and sends information to the other instruments via the bus. Instrument C is a control device which also 'listens' and 'talks' to the other instruments via the bus.

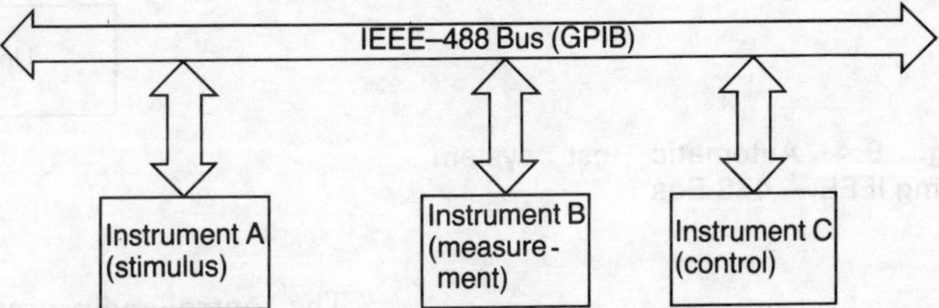

Fig. 9.3 The use of a Standard Bus IEEE — 488

Modern programmable instruments have standard bus interface connectors to enable them to be used as an automatic test equipment (ATE) in an automated test system. Building up an

ATE system, using programmable instruments fitted with standard interface circuitry, becomes fairly straightforward. Individual instruments are linked together by cables with special 'piggyback' connectors. These have male and female termination at either end and a simple lock-screw mechanism enabling cables to be stacked two or three high on top of each other. While the standard bus makes it very easy to connect various instruments together, the test system engineer will still have to define the problem, select the necessary instruments, controllers, and other peripheral devices as well as integrate the system and write the test programme.

Figure 9.4 shows a typical ATS using a standard bus for interface purposes. The principle of operation of a GPIB-based test system is the same as that for the automatic tester described earlier. The test programme is stored in 'programme memory' which is fed into the control unit via the bus.

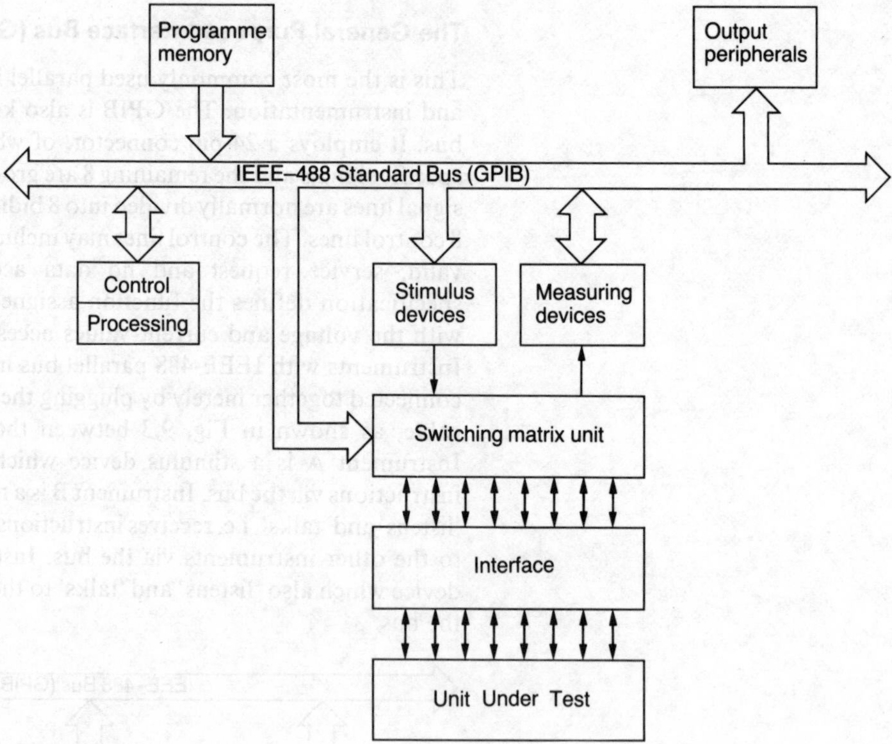

Fig. 9.4 Automatic test system using IEEE — 488 Bus

The control and processing unit manages the whole system by controlling the other units via the bus. Its main functions are as follows:

1. Setting and connecting the stimulus devices to the appropriate test points on the UUT.

2. Setting and connecting the measuring devices to the appropriate test points on the UUT.
3. Results processing, e.g. carrying out comparisons with normal readings and calculations.
4. Transferring the result to peripheral output devices.

For each test, the control and processing unit ensures the appropriate connection to the UUT by setting the switching matrix unit. The connection to the UUT is carried out via an interface or adaptor. The interface may itself be programmable to enable the ATE system to test analogue as well as digital units, and in the case of digital test systems, to enable TTL and CMOS logic boards to be tested, as will be explained later.

Requirements for Automatic Test Equipment

Each unit or device connected to the bus in the system may be considered as an ATE in its own right, e.g. power supply, pulse generator, DVM and CRO.

Complete Automatic Test Systems are also produced as individual ATEs. Such equipment incorporates the essential elements of the test system shown in Fig. 9.4 and may thus be used directly for test purposes. They may be expanded by connecting other ATE elements on an interface bus in the normal way.

Automatic Test Equipment should have the following principal features:

1. Programmability, i.e. it may have its setting and operation controlled by a control unit.
2. Digital output.
3. Standard bus interface for direct connection to other ATEs.

Automatic Testing

Advantages

1. Reduces the demand for skilled test operators.
2. Reduces the chance of human error.
3. Provides more consistent and accurate results.
4. Increases speed of testing.
5. Permits the performance of more complex test procedures.
6. Offers the opportunity for processing the result into a more suitable form.
7. Offers the possibility for self-testing.

The principal reason for using automatic testing is economy. Testing costs in manufacture may be reduced by the use of ATE (a) by employing unskilled and thus lower paid test operators and (b) through increased throughput. This, however, has to be counterbalanced by the disadvantages of automatic testing.

Disadvantages

1. Requires highly skilled test and programming engineers to plan and programme the test system.
2. High initial cost of the system.
3. Necessity to identify all test needs and possible faults prior to putting the system into operation.
4. Relative inflexibility of the system as compared with manual testing, where the test engineer may vary the test procedure to suit the particular faulty symptom.
5. The need for complex and expensive interface to provide access to the UUT.
6. More complex than manual test systems, and hence less reliable.

The use of a Computer

Automatic test systems are very amenable to the use of microprocessors or computers in general. The bus structure employed is easily transferable to computerized systems.

There are two ways in which a computer may be employed in an ATE system. The first is where a computer is used merely as the controller in a bus-structured system. This is known as computer-controlled ATE system. The second is the computer-based system, where the test system is structured around the computer.

Computer-controlled ATE system

Figure 9.5 shows a computer-controlled ATE system. The computer, which may be a personal computer, is used as the central control and processing unit. It is connected to the various elements of the system, i.e. the stimulus and measuring devices and the switching matrix unit via a standard GPIB (IEEE-488) bus. Other peripheral units, such as a keyboard, display, printer, and floppy disc are connected to the computer via individual RS 232 series bus connectors. The operation of the system is identical to that described earlier for a bus-structured ATE system. The computer carries out a sequence of tests in accordance with a test programme. It also compares the readings with expected responses obtained from a known-good unit, carries out necessary calibration of results, and processes them into a more suitable form before feeding them for further processing, display, print or storage. The programme may be stored in a peripheral memory

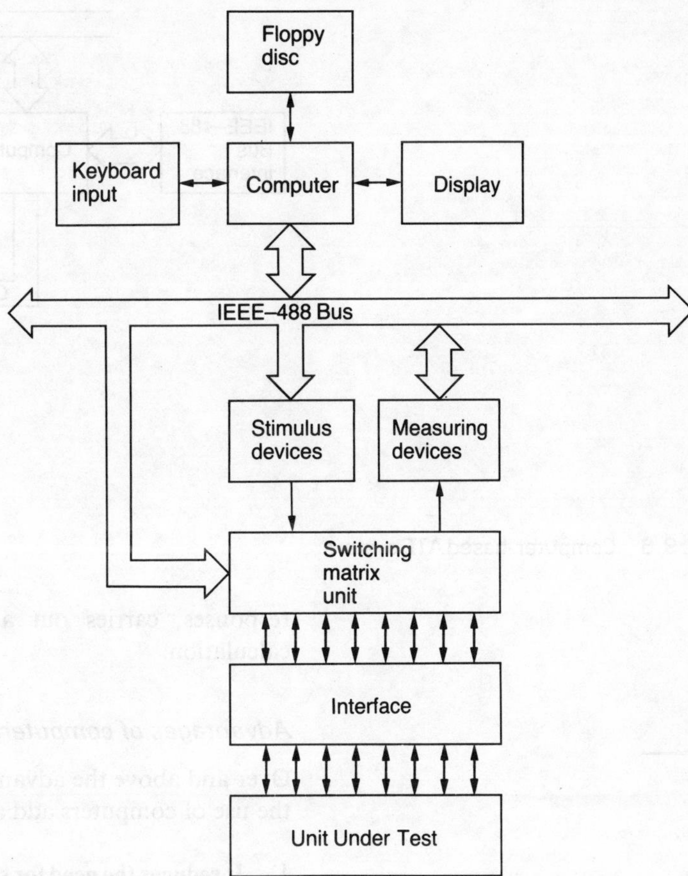

Fig. 9.5 Computer-controlled ATE system

such as a floppy disc or a magnetic tape, or it may be fed directly into the computer via the keyboard.

Computer-based ATE

Automatic test systems employing computers as the centre of the system are increasingly employed over a wide range of applications. In this type, the computer is used as the basis for measurement, as well as for the generation of input test signals, computation of output responses and manipulation of results. Figure 9.6 shows a simplified block diagram for a computer-based ATE. Test programmes are provided by either external or internal memory stores. For each test, the computer generates the required test input response in a digital coded synthesized format which is converted into a time-related voltage or current waveform by the D-to-A converter. These signals are applied to the UTT via the switching matrix unit, and the interface. The resulting test responses are routed via the switching unit back to the computer by the use of an A-to-D converter. The computer analyses the

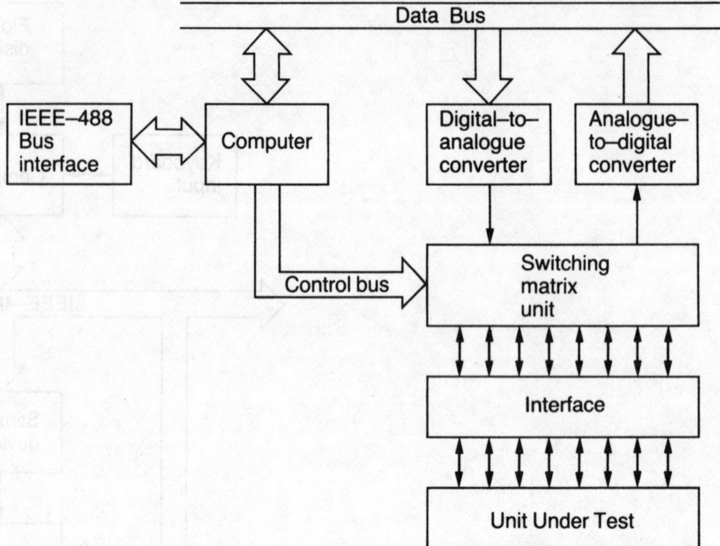

Fig. 9.6 Computer-based ATE system

responses, carries out a variety of data manipulation and calculation.

Advantages of computer-based ATE

Over and above the advantages of ATE systems outlined earlier, the use of computers add a number of other advantages:

1. **It reduces the need for separate programmable stimulus devices.** Stimulus signals are generated by software, where digital replicas of waveforms are stored in memory and called forward whenever necessary.
2. **Data manipulation.** Computers allow more complex calculations and other manipulation to be carried out quickly and accurately. They also allow the storage of digital replicas of waveforms, which may be called forward for use as test signals or for comparison purposes.
3. **Programme flexibility.** Computers provide a wide choice of method of testing. Changes require a change in software only, i.e. a change in programme without any change in the hardware of the system.
4. **Speed.** Computer-based systems are very fast in carrying out the test functions as well as producing the results.
5. **Low cost and small size.**

10 Use of automatic test equipment (ATE)

The manufacture of an electronic system goes through a series of stages from board and component purchase, board assembly to system assembly before going into the field for use by a customer. The manufacturing process also contains a series of testing activities performed at each stage of manufacture.

While the final test on a product is usually mandatory to ensure that the quality of the product meets the customer's requirements, the preceding intermediate test stages are also necessary as a confidence check to eliminate assembly and process errors, thus reducing the necessity to fault-find at the final stage.

The cost of finding a fault increases dramatically as testing is moved to the later stage of the manufacturing process. This is particularly true in the manufacture of modern complex electronic equipment. Thus testing is acquiring a more important place in the manufacturing process and is usually introduced in the initial stage, where test requirements are forming an essential part of design and development.

The manufacturing process

There are three distinct phases in the life cycle of an electronic system, namely design, manufacture, and field-use. Each of these phases requires some form of testing. During the design phase, the purpose of testing is to validate the design and ensure that it meets the required specifications. During manufacture, the emphasis is on fault finding, following which the unit under test may or may not be repaired. During field-use, the purpose of testing is fault finding and repair in order to return the system to working order as soon as possible.

Figure 10.1 shows a schematic diagram showing the stages of testing in the manufacture of an electronic system. The manufacturing process begins with 'incoming devices' stage where the devices and components, including bare printed circuit boards, are acquired from outside suppliers or other parts of the firm. The next stage, 'board assembly', involves the insertion and soldering of devices and components on to the printed circuit board (PCB)

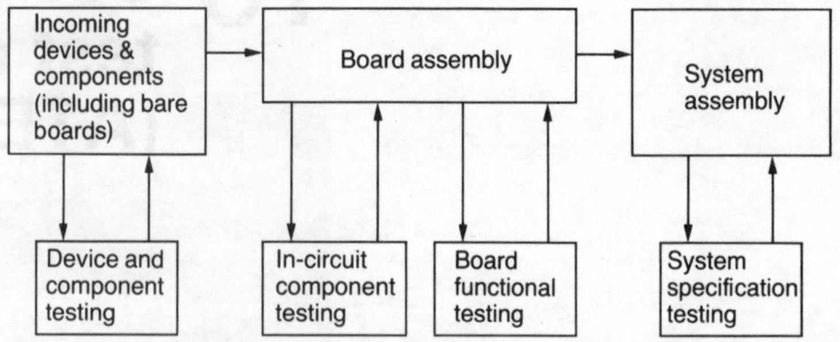

Fig. 10.1 Testing stages in manufacture

to produce a complete functioning board. The third and final stage is 'system assembly', where the completed PCBs are assembled together to form the complete system. At each stage, there is one or more testing activity. For small scale manufacture (less than 100 PCBs a week) testing may be carried out manually. However, for medium or large scale manufacture, automatic test equipments are used.

Testing

Device, component and bare board testing

Device and component testing is carried out on individual components before insertion on to the PCB. It may be a simple test on basic parameters of a transistor, analogue IC, or a simple truth-table test on digital ICs, or a full parametric test including temperature recycling and tolerances. Such tests can be carried out by a general purpose ATE which may be programmed for testing a variety of devices.

Bare board testing involves checking the continuity of the copper track on the printed circuit board to test for open tracks or short circuits between tracks. An automatic tester for this purpose requires an interface, which will make contact with a large number of internal test points on the board. Such an interface is known as a bed-of-nails fixture. A bed-of-nails fixture is a multi-probe interface consisting of a group of spring-loaded pins which connect to appropriate points on the board. The tester is programmed to measure the resistance between various test points to check for continuity and short circuits.

In-circuit testing

This form of testing seeks to check individual components and devices on the board, such as resistors, capacitors, diodes, transistors, gates, as well as ICs such as RAM and ROM. The purpose of in-circuit testing is to ensure that the right components and devices having the specified values, parameters or truth tables are mounted in the correct place on the PCB and in the correct direction. An automatic tester for this purpose will also require a

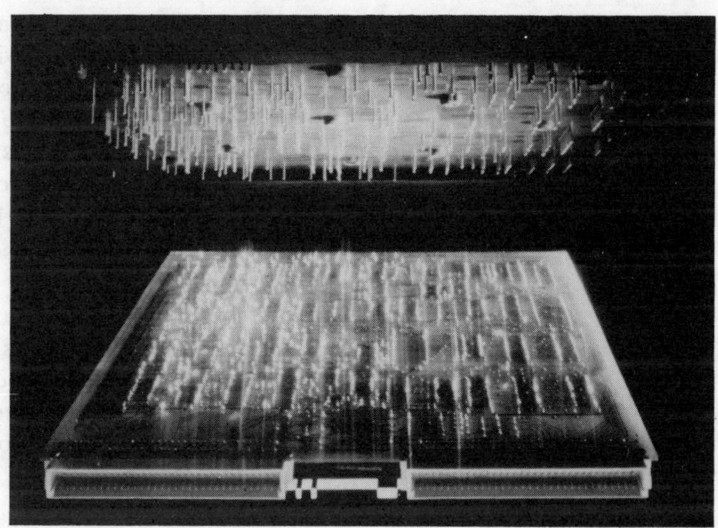

Fig. 10.2 Bed-of-nails interface fixture (Courtesy Marconi Instruments)

bed-of-nails interface fixture to probe into internal test points or nodes on the PCB (Fig. 10.2).

Board functional testing

Functional testing follows and complements the in-circuit testing described above. While the in-circuit testing isolates and tests individual components and devices, functional testing checks the overall function of the completed board assembly. An automatic functional tester will normally access the PCB via an edge connector without the need for an expensive bed-of-nails fixture.

System testing

When the boards have been assembled and tested to an acceptable standard, they are assembled to form a complete system. The completed system is then tested to ensure that it meets the required specifications. The purpose of 'system testing' is mainly to check that the system meets its design specifications. General purpose ATE do not exist for this type of test. Each system dictates its own system-level test requirements, based on the design specifications.

Types of ATE

There are two main types of ATE in use in product testing and field service: the in-circuit ATE and the functional ATE. Some automatic test equipments combine both types, usually in the form of a functional tester with in-circuit test facilities.

In-circuit ATE

These test the components on an assembled printed circuit board to determine their actual true value, via a bed-of-nails interface fixture or jig. The board under test (BUT) is forced down on to the bed-of-nails and contact with the spring-loaded pins is maintained by a pneumatic or a vacuum force. The values of individual components, both passive and active, are sequentially measured in-circuit, and these values are checked against stored standards to isolate faulty ones. An in-circuit tester may identify the following faults on a printed circuit board:

1. Short circuits due to soldering or poor lay-out.
2. Unsoldered joints.
3. Faulty components.
4. Incorrect components fitted.
5. Incorrect orientation of components.
6. Incorrectly coded components.
7. Missing components or links.
8. Incorrect wiring.
9. Open-circuited tracks.

Each fault is isolated and reported in a print-out or display, and the whole operation is completed within a minute or so, depending on the number and type of components on the PCB.

Figure 10.3 shows a simplified block diagram for an in-circuit ATE for analogue testing purposes. (Testers for digital printed circuit boards will be considered in the next chapter.) The computer in Fig. 10.3 controls the tester in the manner explained in Chapter 9. Stimulus signals are routed to appropriate test points

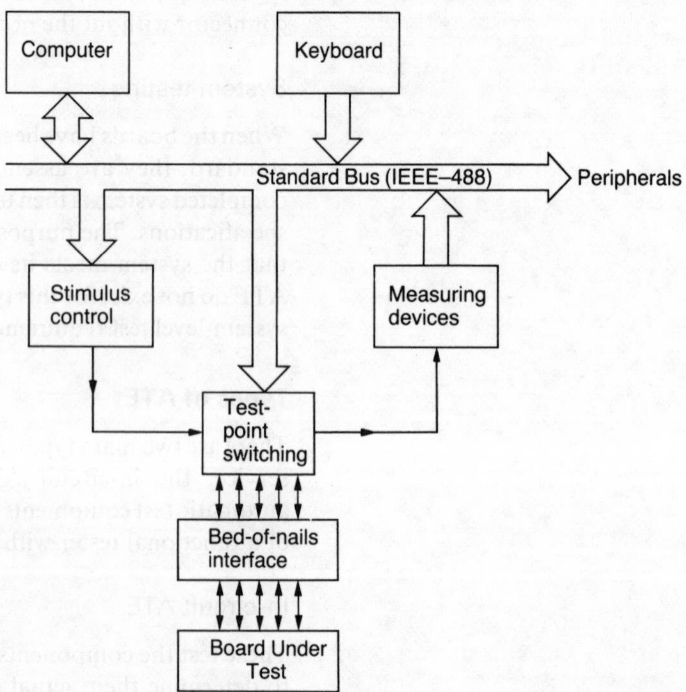

Fig. 10.3 In-circuit test for analogue boards

on the BUT, through the switching unit and the bed-of-nails interface fixture. The switching is of the matrix type using mercury-wetted reed relays to meet the necessary requirement of isolation when open, and low series impedance when closed. Multiplexing is also possible, as is explained in Chapter 11.

Responses are routed via the interface fixture and the switching unit to the measuring device. Results are fed to the computer for calculation, comparison and processing. The ATE in Fig. 10.3 may be used to carry out in-circuit measurements on passive components such as resistors, capacitors and diodes, as well as active components such as transistors and analogue ICs.

Test results, as well as being printed on to a 'repair ticket' indicating the faulty components, can be recorded on disc for later analysis. Computer tabulations of fault incidence can be produced, indicating possible faulty component batches, repeated assembly faults, process errors and other faults in manufacture, providing useful statistics for quality control of the production process.

Resistance Measurement

To measure the value of passive components on a PCB, contact is made via the bed-of-nails to the two terminals of the component. A signal, e.g. a direct voltage for a resistor or a sinewave for a capacitor, is then fed into the component and measurement of the true value of the component is made.

Figure 10.4(a) shows the method used for resistance measure-

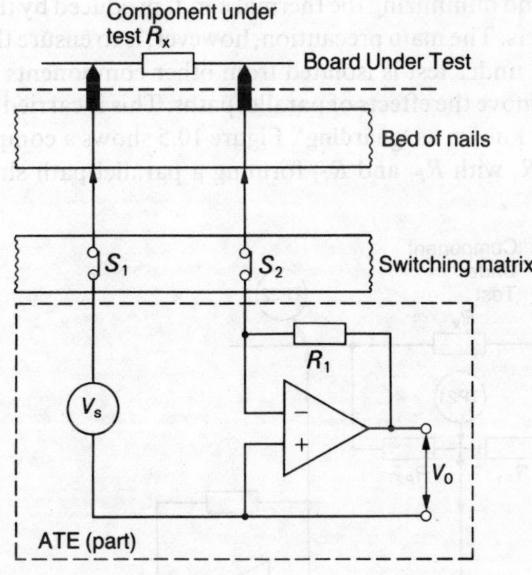

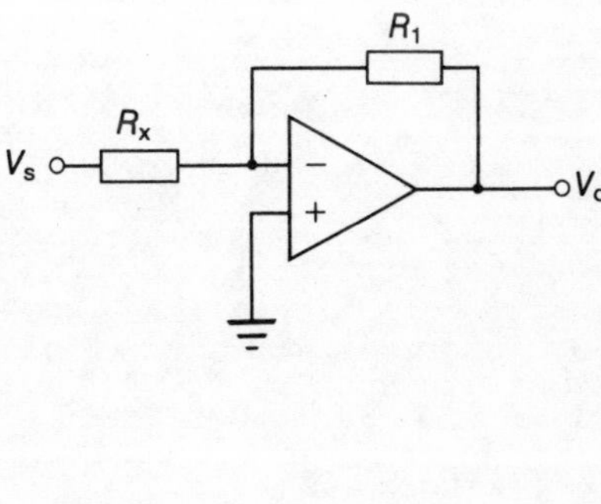

Fig. 10.4 In-circuit measurement of resistance

ment. Switches S_1 and S_2 on the switching unit are closed, so that contact is made to the two ends of the component under test, R_x, via the bed-of-nails interface. Stimulus voltage V_s is fed into R_x and operational amplifier output V_o is measured. The stimulus voltage is limited to about 200 mV to ensure that adjacent semiconductors do not conduct. Figure 10.4(b) reproduces the circuit diagram for 10.4(a). Resistor R_1 is the range resistance selected for the particular measurement. The value of the output response V_o is thus determined by the stimulus voltage level and the gain of the amplifier.

$$\text{Gain} = \frac{V_o}{V_s} = \frac{R_1}{R_X} \text{ giving}$$

$$R_X = \frac{R_1 V_S}{V_o}$$

With R_1 and V_s set at predetermined values, R_x is proportional to the reciprocal of the output response voltage. The computer carries out this simple conversion to find the true value of the resistor and subsequently checks it against the correct value. A difference outside the accepted tolerance band is indicated as a fault on a print-out.

Several precautions have to be taken to ensure that the measured value is the true value of the resistor. Such precautions include reducing the resistance of the contact switches to a minimum and minimizing the thermal e.m.f. produced by the reed relay contacts. The main precaution, however, is to ensure that the component under test is isolated from other components on the board to remove the effects of parallel paths. This is carried out by a technique known as **'guarding'**. Figure 10.5 shows a component under test R_x with R_{P1} and R_{P2} forming a parallel path shunting

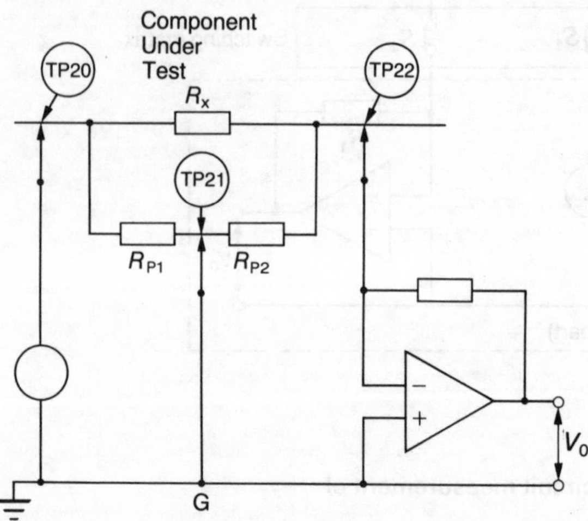

Fig. 10.5 'Guarding' in In-circuit measurement of resistance

resistance. A straightforward resistance measurement across TP20 and TP22 will give an incorrect value for R_x. The unknown resistor R_x must be isolated from R_{P1} and R_{P2} before its resistance may be measured accurately. This may be carried out by connecting TP21 to a 'guard' point G which is at earth potential. In this way the effect of R_{P1} and R_{P2} is negligible with virtually all the current flowing from R_x going to the operational amplifier. On one hand, the loading effect of R_{P1} is negligible because of the very low resistance of the power supply providing the stimulus voltage. On the other hand R_{P2} is earthed on one side and is at 'virtual earth' at the operational amplifier end thus taking no current. In practice, parallel paths are more complex and 'guarding' may not be as simple as that shown in Fig. 10.5. In such cases, what is known as 'extended guarding' is employed to overcome a variety of errors introduced by other resistances such as lead resistance and voltage source resistance.

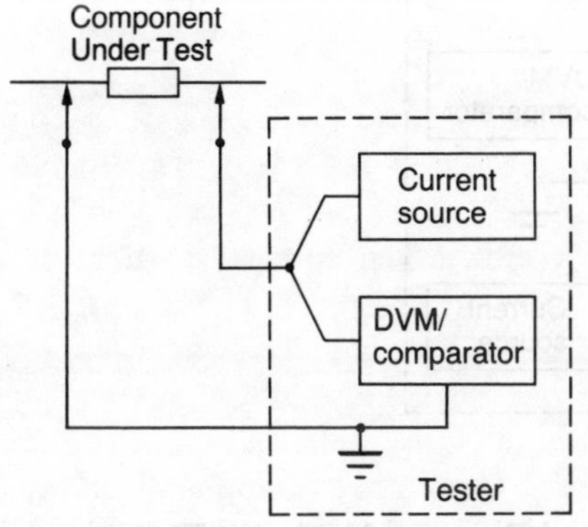

Fig. 10.6 In-circuit testing for shorts and opens

Testing for short and open circuits

One method of checking for short and open circuits is shown in Fig. 10.6. A constant current source in the tester forces a suitable current, say 10 mA into the component under test. The voltage developed across the component is then measured by a DVM, compared with expected value, and a Pass/Fail decision is then made. The same method can be used for testing components such as diodes and transistor junctions. In such cases, the current provided by the current source is used to forward bias the junction of a transistor for measurement of the forward resistance.

Effect of parallel capacitors

Test routines must be designed to take account of the effect of a capacitor connected across a component under test, particularly in such tests as an open circuit test of a diode junction reverse resistance measurement. In the latter the tester will measure a progressively increasing resistance as the capacitor charges up. Also, provisions must be made to ensure that all capacitors are discharged before the test commences.

Active Component Testing

Testing active components, such as transistors, digital and linear ICs or LSI chips such as RAM and ROM, must be carried out under power-up conditions, i.e. the component must be connected to an appropriate power source. During this process, other components or even the whole board may be powered-up. In all cases, low power levels are used (e.g. 50% of normal) to avoid putting other components adjacent to the component under test under abnormal stress, thus ageing them especially if the component being tested is likely to suffer from a catastrophic fault such as a short circuit. The in-circuit tester measures one or more important parameters of the active component under test, e.g. static current gain, leakage current of a transistor, and/or saturation conditions.

Figure 10.7 shows one method of checking transistor saturation conditions, polarity and gain. The transistor under test is forward biased by forcing a current (say 10 mA) into its base-emitter junction. The collector is fed with a supply voltage V_{cc} (say, 15 V), via a collector load resistor R_c (say 1.5 kΩ). These conditions ensure that the transistor is fully conducting. The resultant collector voltage is measured, compared with the expected value (a good transistor would give a collector voltage of approximately 1.4 V) and a Pass/Fail indication is given.

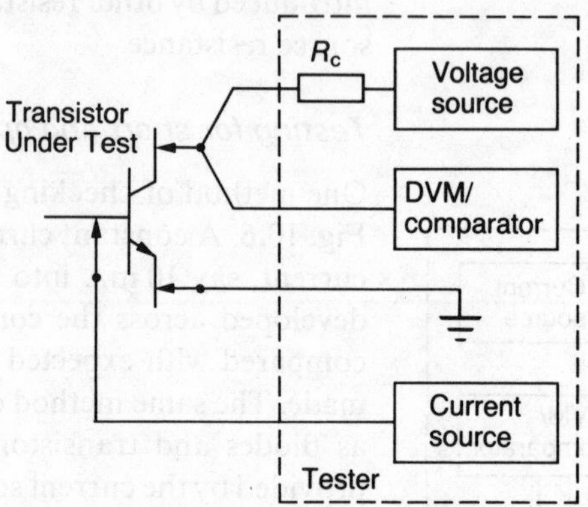

Fig. 10.7 In-circuit testing of transistors

Requirements for a General Purpose In-circuit Tester

A general purpose in-circuit tester should have the following:

1. Measurement capabilities:
   - Track continuity.
   - Track isolation.
   - Resistors from below 1Ω to over 10 MΩ.
   - Capacitors from below 10 pF to over 1600 μF.
   - Inductors from below 100 μH to over 25 H.
   - Diodes forward voltage drop and leakage current.
   - Zener diodes.
   - Transistors, both bipolar and fet.
   - Relays.
   - Linear ICs.
   - Digital ICs.
2. Facilities to change the bed-of-nails interface fixture with ease.
3. Direct programming capability both for programme modification or programme generation.

Advantages and Disadvantages of In-circuit Testers

Advantages

1. Lower initial cost of the system compared with functional testers.
2. Easy to operate.
3. Easy to programme.
4. Very effective in isolating production faults, such as short and open circuits, missing components and wrong value components.

Disadvantages

1. High cost of interface, due to the need for individual bed-of-nails fixture for each type of board to be tested.
2. Requires vacuum or pneumatic power source to operate the interface fixture.
3. Does not test the dynamic performance of the components. Hence, even if all the components were verified to be sound, the board may still not function correctly under normal operating conditions. Hence, fault coverage, i.e. the number of faults detected, is relatively low (often in the region of 80–90%).

Functional ATE

A functional tester is used to evaluate the performance of the board under test under normal operating stimulus. Access to the board is normally achieved via the edge connector, making the design and cost of interface connectors simple and cheap compared with the bed-of-nails fixture. In some cases, additional connections may be needed, depending on the design of the board. Such extra connections may be provided by chip probes or connectors.

The functional tester provides a very fast indication on whether the PCB is sound or faulty. In essence, it provides the basic **Go/No-Go** test on the board. A No-Go result indicates the presence of hardware failure, caused by faults in PCB manufacture, faulty ICs, faulty IC pin connections, faults in assembly or mechanism such as switches. The Go/No-Go test may indicate the area of the fault, but normally without enough precision to enable repairs to be carried out. For this to be achieved, further diagnostic procedures must be carried out. This may involve monitoring and examining waveforms using a digitizing programmable oscilloscope, controlled by the tester via the IEEE-488 bus. In the case of a digital board under test, a **'roving probe'** may be used to verify response at various internal nodes under the direction of the functional tester itself.

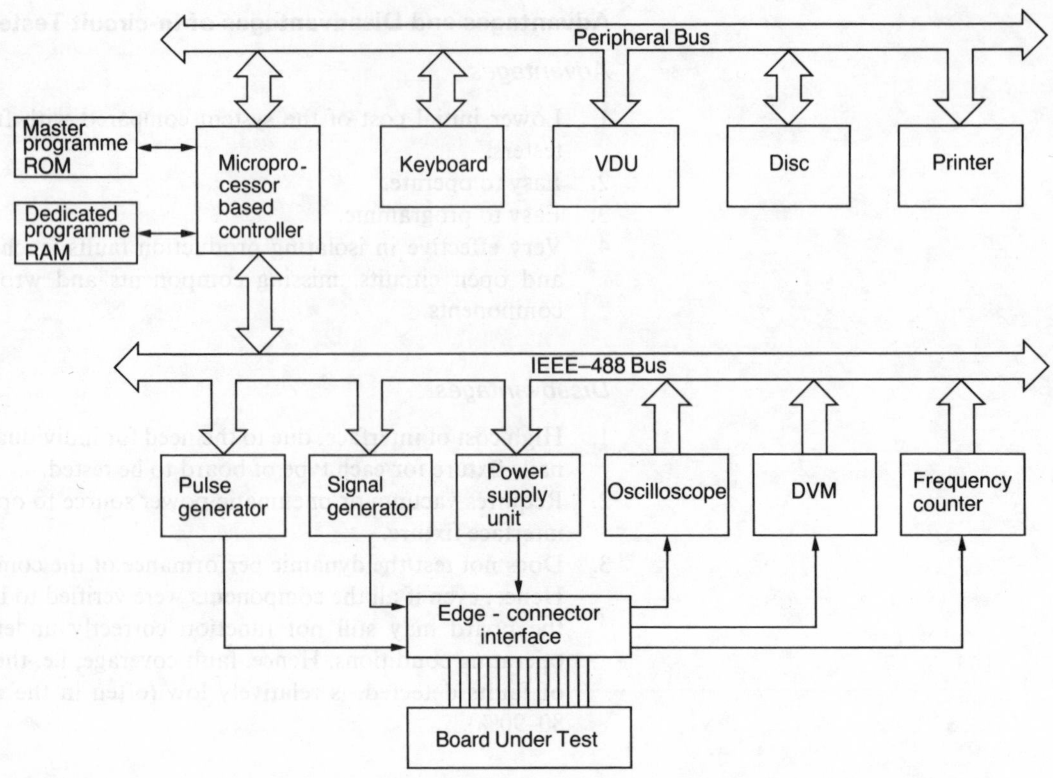

Fig. 10.8 Functional tester for analogue boards

Functional testers for digital- and microprocessor-based boards will be considered in detail in Chapter 11.

Figure 10.8 shows a block diagram of a functional tester for analogue boards. Two buses are shown: the IEEE-488 instrumentation bus for interfacing the programmable instruments, and the peripheral bus for interfacing the peripherals to the microprocessor-based controller. Two memory stores are shown: a permanent ROM store for the master programme containing the basic programme requirements, and arrangements such as interaction with the keyboard operator or for calculations and display of results. The RAM chip stores the programme dedicated for the particular board to be tested.

The stimulus signals are produced by the pulse or signal generator under direction of the controller. Other devices may be added. The board is powered up by a programmable power supply unit. These signals are fed into the board under test via an edge connector interface. (Other connections may be made to other test points if necessary.) Output responses are picked up from the board's edge connector and routed via the interface to one or more of the measuring devices. The controller receives the measured results, compares them with those expected from a good board and indicates the results. Further detailed tests to identify the precise fault may be carried out manually, either under the control of the operator using the keyboard, or under instructions from the tester by directing the operator to the steps to be taken. Such steps may include observing and making measurements on waveforms using the oscilloscope, or measuring voltage levels or frequencies at various stages of the test programme, or at other internal test points. Following each step, and depending on the results obtained, the tester will direct the operator to the next step to be taken, and so on, until the faulty component and the nature of the fault is identified.

Advantages of functional testers

1. Because a functional tester verifies the actual operating specifications of the board under test, it has a high fault coverage of between 90–98%.
2. Functional testing is significantly faster than in-circuit testing where every component has to be tested individually.
3. The edge connector interface is simple to design and cheap to make.

Disadvantages of functional testers

1. Complex and expensive.
2. More complex to programme.
3. Isolating the fault in a faulty board is difficult and time-consuming.

Comparison between In-circuit and Functional Testers

Automatic testers are undergoing major developments. The following table provides typical values for comparison purposes.

	In-circuit	*Functional*
Cost	Low (£50,000–£180,000)	High (£100,000 upwards)
Interface fixture	Complex and expensive	Simple and cheap
Programming time	2–4 weeks	4–16 weeks
Test time (Go/No Go)	15–60 s	2–45 s
Diagnosis time	10–60 s	4–10 mins
Overall fault coverage	80–90%	90–98%

11 Digital board ATE

Digital board testing may be carried out in the two ways mentioned in Chapter 10, namely in-circuit and functional testing. In-circuit testing of a digital PCB involves testing individual digital devices such as simple gates, JK flip-flops, binary counters, or more complex memory chips. In-circuit testing digital boards is, in reality, therefore, testing the function of the device under test (DUT). Functional board testing, on the other hand, involves the evaluation of the function of the board by applying a set of digital stimulus signals to the board's edge connector, to verify that the digital responses generated by the board are correct.

In-circuit Testing of Digital Boards

The first task of evaluating the DUT is to write a test programme. This programme provides a sequence of logic pulses, known as a test pattern, to the input pins of the DUT, and at the same time captures the response pattern at the output. This data is used for evaluation of the state of the DUT, and the procedure is known as test-pattern generation. The second task is to evaluate the effectiveness of the test pattern, i.e. to ensure that it can detect all possible faults. This may mean changing the original test pattern to improve the fault coverage of the test programme. When the test pattern is finalized, it is then used in practical or simulated situations to discover its effectiveness in fault detection.

Test-pattern generation

There are two basic methods for writing a test pattern. The first is the *functional method* which takes the device through all its functions to ensure that it generates the expected output responses. For a simple gate, it means going through its truth table. The second method is '*fault-derived*' or '*fault-orientated*' based on providing a sequence of tests to detect the presence of all possible faults. This method begins by drawing up a fault list or dictionary outlining all possible faults and then devising a distinctive test to check the presence of each fault.

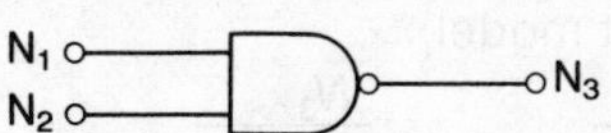

Fig. 11.1 Two-input NAND gate

Example NAND Gate

Figure 11.1 shows a 2-input NAND gate with nodes N_1 and N_2 as the inputs and node N_3 as the output. The functional test pattern consists of a sequence of input logic states taking the gate through its truth table.

Table 11.1

Truth table for NAND gate

N_1	N_2	N_3
0	0	1
0	1	1
1	0	1
1	1	0

From the truth table, it follows that the test pattern or test vector necessary at each node is as follows:

Node N_1 0011
Node N_2 0101
and the expected output pattern is

Node N_3 1110

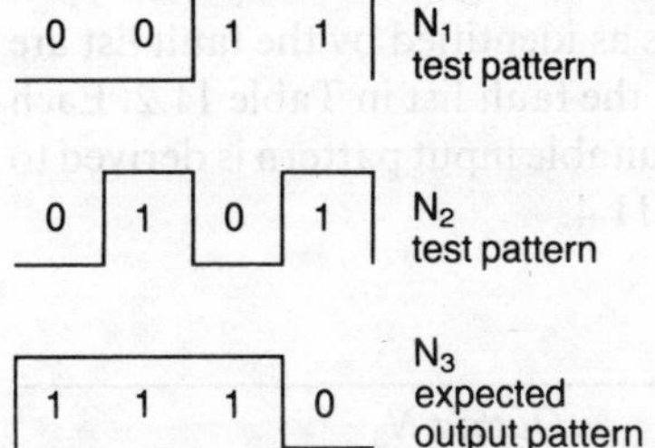

Fig. 11.2 Test and response patterns for a good NAND gate

Time waveforms for the test and the expected response patterns are shown in Fig. 11.2. The tester is, therefore, required to generate the waveform patterns shown, and inject them into the inputs of the gate at N_1 and N_2 simultaneously. It is also required to receive the output response pattern at N_3. If the response pattern is different from that shown, then the gate is faulty.

The number of tests required for the 2-input NAND gate are $2^2 = 4$. In general, for n primary inputs to a gate (or a combination of gates), the number of tests required to go through the truth table is 2^n. For a 3-input gate, the number of tests required is $2^3 = 8$ and so on. The number of tests thus grows very rapidly as the number of inputs increases, which makes this type of test-pattern generation very time-consuming and even impractical in some cases.

The number of tests may be reduced without reducing the fault coverage. In a functional test pattern, one or more tests are carried out which add no more information about the detection of a possible fault. This is shown by looking at Tables 11.2 and 11.3. Table 11.2 shows a fault list based on a 'stuck-at' model. This is the most popular model which assumes that all faults will result in one or more nodes stuck at logic level 1 (s-a-1), or stuck at logic level 0 (s-a-0). Fault coverage is shown in Table 11.3. For each test sequence, the test pattern is shown together with the expected output of a sound gate, e.g. for test sequence 2 the input pattern is 01 and expected output is 1. If the output is faulty, i.e. N_3 is 0, then one possible fault is N_3 s-a-0. Another possible fault is N_1 s-a-1. In the N_1 s-a-1 case both N_1 and N_2 are at 1 giving an output of 0. Each test covers at least one fault. However, fault N_3 s-a-0 is covered

Table 11.2

Fault list (stuck-at model)

N_1	N_2	N_3
s.a.0.	s.a.0.	s.a.0.
s.a.1.	s.a.1.	s.a.1.

Table 11.3

Test sequence	Input pattern N_1	N_2	Expected output N_3	Faulty output N_3	Fault covered N_1	N_2	N_3
1	0	0	1	0			s.a.0
2	0	1	1	0	s.a.1		s.a.0
3	1	0	1	0		s.a.1	s.a.0
4	1	1	0	1	s.a.0	s.a.0	s.a.1

three times: test sequences 1, 2 and 3. Since test sequences 2 and 3 cover faults N_1 s-a-0 and N_2 s-a-1 respectively as well as N_3 s-a-0, then test sequence 1 is redundant.

Such redundant tests may be avoided by employing a fault-based method for test pattern generation. Using this strategy, only the tests necessary to cover the faults as identified by the fault list are carried out. The starting point is the fault list in Table 11.2. Each fault is then taken in turn and a suitable input pattern is derived to test for each, as shown in Table 11.4.

Table 11.4

Test sequence	Fault list Node	Fault	Input pattern N_1	N_2	Output N_3 Expected	Faulty	Comments
A	N_1	s.a.1	0	1	1	0	
B	N_1	s.a.0	1	1	0	1	
C	N_2	s.a.1	1	0	1	0	
D	N_2	s.a.0	1	1	0	1	Same as B
E	N_3	s.a.1	1	1	0	1	Same as B
F	N_3	s.a.0	0	1	1	0	Same as A

The number of tests necessary is, therefore, reduced to three only, namely:

Test sequence	Input N_1	N_2	Expected output N_3
A	0	1	1
B	1	1	0
C	1	0	1

Test vectors

Each test sequence consists of a set of stimulus and response patterns, e.g. test sequence A in Table 11.4 consisting of stimulus 0 and 1 applied to N_1 and N_2 and response 1 at N_3. These stimulus/response patterns are known as **vectors**, which may be filed in memory to be retrieved by simply recalling the vector address. This applies equally to single gates as well as combinational logic or ICs.

Pin Electronics

As explained earlier, an in-circuit tester employs a bed-of-nails interface. The 'nails' on the bed-of-nails are known as pins. Each pin makes contact with a particular node on the BUT. The pin may be used to drive a node to logic HIGH or LOW, or to high impedance when using a tristate device. Alternatively it may be used to receive and detect the logic response at a node. The pin therefore provides a bidirectional input/output contact with the board. Each pin is controlled by its own 'channel', as shown in Fig. 11.3. Each channel contains a buffer which provides the bidirectional path between the board and the tester as well as other

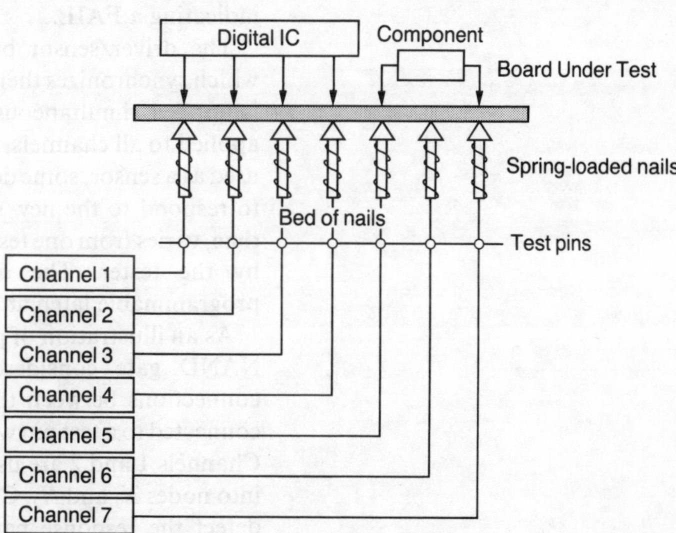

Fig. 11.3 'Pin electronics' ATE system

electronic circuitry to control the pin. The circuitry of the channel is known as pin or channel electronics, i.e. the electronics behind each test pin. The bidirectional contact is provided by the driver/sensor buffer shown in Fig. 11.4. The buffer consists of two operational amplifiers, used as a driver and a sensor. In the driver state when the pin is being used to provide a stimulus pattern to the node, the driver amplifier is enabled. The data input provides the

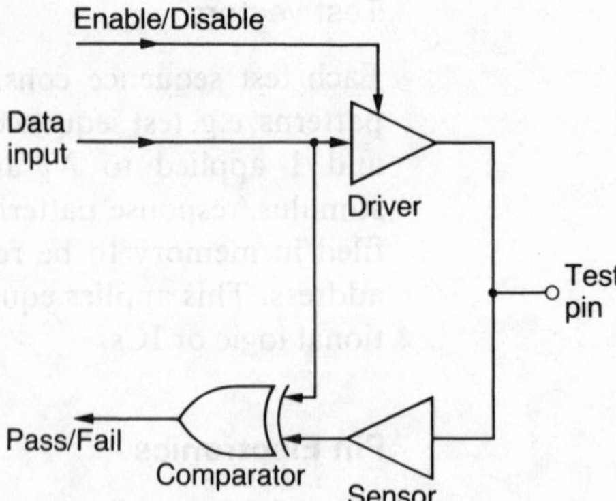

Fig. 11.4 Basic bidirectional buffer

appropriate test pattern fed into the node via the amplifier and the test pin. When used as a sensor, the driver amplifier is disabled. The sensor amplifier then receives and detects the response pattern of the node and feeds it into the 2-input Exclusive-OR gate being used as a comparator. The other input to the comparator is the anticipated response pattern provided by the data input. If the two inputs are the same, the output from the comparator remains at logic '0' indicating a PASS. Any difference between the two inputs to the comparator will be represented by logic '1' at its output, indicating a FAIL.

The driver/sensor buffers are controlled by a timing clock which synchronizes their operation to ensure that the test stimulus is applied simultaneously to all nodes under test. This clock is applied to all channels, whether used as drivers or sensors. When used as a sensor, some delay is necessary to allow time for the DUT to respond to the new stimulus values. This delay, called **strobe time**, varies from one test routine to another, and is programmable by the tester. The delay may be produced by adding a programmable latch at the output of the comparator.

As an illustration of pin electronics, consider the testing of the NAND gate considered previously. Figure 11.5 shows the connections between the DUT and the test pins. Each node is connected to a test pin which is backed by a driver/sensor channel. Channels 1 and 2 are used as drivers to feed the stimulus pattern into nodes N_1 and N_2. Channel 3 is used as a sensor to receive and detect the response pattern and compare it with the expected response to indicate Pass or Fail. Using the fault-based test devised earlier, the programme consists of three test sequences:

	N_1	N_2	N_3
Sequence A	0	1	1
Sequence B	1	1	0
Sequence C	1	0	1

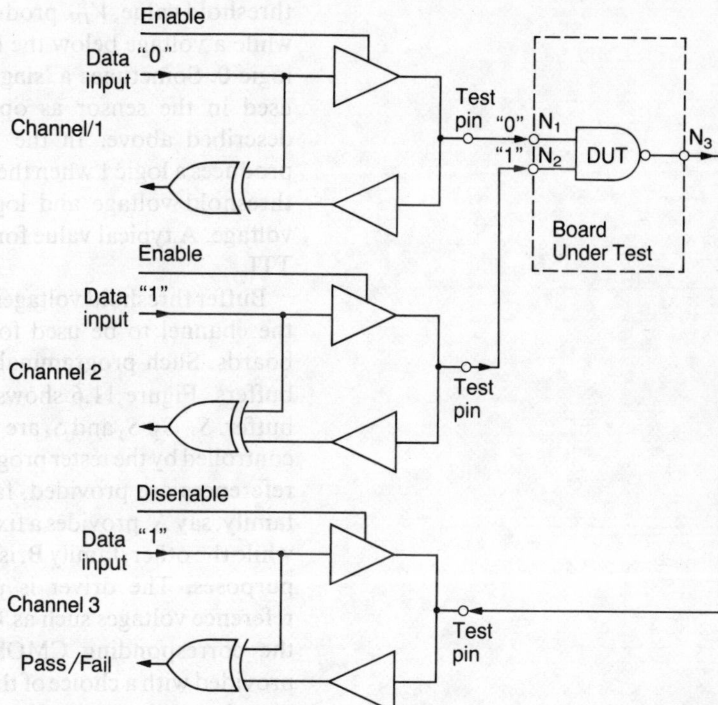

Fig. 11.5 Pin electronics testing applied to a NAND gate

Each sequence is placed on the data input lines of the three channels simultaneously. Thus for Sequence A, channel 1 data input is set to logic '0', channel 2 to logic '1' and channel 3 to logic '1'. The gate under test thus receives a stimulus of logic '0' to N_1 and logic '1' to N_2. The logic output level at N_3 is received by the test pin and detected by the sensor amplifier. The comparator of channel 3 thus receives two inputs: logic '1' from the input data indicating the expected response at N_3 and the actual logic level at N_3. If the two inputs are the same, the comparator produces a logic '0' at its output, indicating a PASS. If the two inputs are different, then the output is logic '1' indicating a FAIL. When test sequence A is completed, the tester moves to test sequence B and so on until the test programme is completed.

Threshold Voltages

Both the driver and sensor amplifiers are provided with the appropriate reference voltages for the type of logic used in the BUT. The driver has two threshold voltage levels HIGH and LOW, V_H and V_L corresponding to logic 1 and logic 0, which for TTL corresponds to 5 V and 0 V respectively. This way, the driver will always produce the correct voltage level at the test pin for the required logic state. The sensor amplifier is provided with two threshold voltages, namely V_{TH} and V_{TL}, which for TTL corresponds to 2.4 V and 0.8 V respectively. Any voltage level above the high threshold value, V_{TH}, produces a logic 1 from the sensor amplifier, while a voltage below the low threshold voltage, V_{TL}, produces a logic 0. Sometimes a **'single threshold'** reference voltage may be used in the sensor as opposed to the **'dual threshold'** system described above. In the 'single threshold' system, the sensor produces a logic 1 when the voltage level at the test pin is above the threshold voltage and logic 0 when it is below the threshold voltage. A typical value for a 'single threshold' system is 2.4 V for TTL.

Buffer threshold voltages are normally programmable to enable the channel to be used for testing both TTL and CMOS logic boards. Such programmable buffers are known as **'dual family'** buffers. Figure 11.6 shows a typical dual threshold, dual family buffer. S_1, S_2, S_3 and S_4 are programmable relay-operated contacts controlled by the tester programme. Two families of programmable references are provided, family A and family B. Normally, one family, say A, provides a fixed reference voltage for TTL purposes, while the other, family B, is a variable voltage reference for CMOS purposes. The driver is provided with a choice of family A reference voltages such as $V_{HA} = 5$ V and $V_{LA} = 0$ V or family B for the corresponding CMOS voltage levels. The sensor is also provided with a choice of threshold voltages from the two families, namely family A with $V_{THA} = 2.4$ V and $V_{TLB} = 0.8$ V and family B for the corresponding CMOS threshold voltage levels.

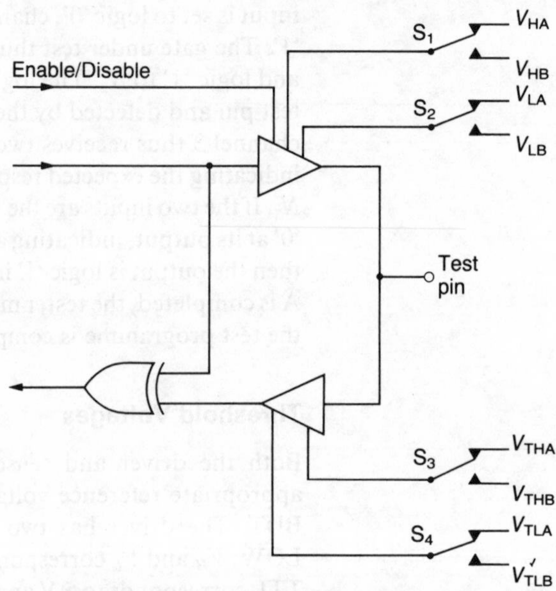

Fig. 11.6 A typical dual threshold, dual family buffer

RAM-backed pin electronics

Complex devices and modern digital circuit design result in larger and more complex digital PCB, which require correspondingly

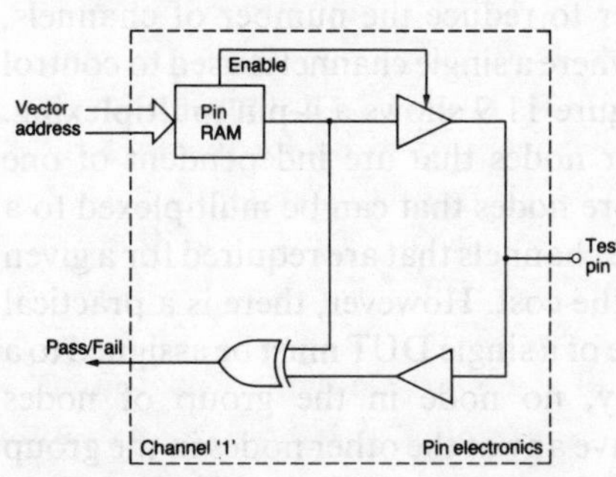

Fig. 11.7 Memory backed pin electronics system

more complex test routines. These complex tests need more pins and more test sequences or vectors. A typical 16-pin TTL device may require about 200 test vectors. However, modern devices, e.g. 64-pin LSI devices, have about 2000 test vectors. The number of data bits required increases dramatically as the complexity of the device grows. The problem is compounded by the fact that there are increasing numbers of such devices on a typical board and each device requires its own test routine. All this information must be created, stored, retrieved and transferred to the test pin. Using the channel arrangement described earlier results in lengthy test time, as the information is downloaded from the main programme processor to each channel. One method of speeding up the execution of the test programme is to use a memory backing for each pin, known as RAM backed pin electronics, as shown in Fig. 11.7. The pin RAM contains the data for each test vector including the driver ENABLE instruction.

Each channel is connected to the vector address bus, as shown in Fig. 11.8. When a vector address is placed on the vector address bus, each pin RAM is instructed to issue the relevant logic level to the driver/sensor buffer. When the test sequence is completed and the results received, the channel control issues the vector address of the next test sequence. In this way, the time required for downloading the test data to the driver/sensor buffer is reduced.

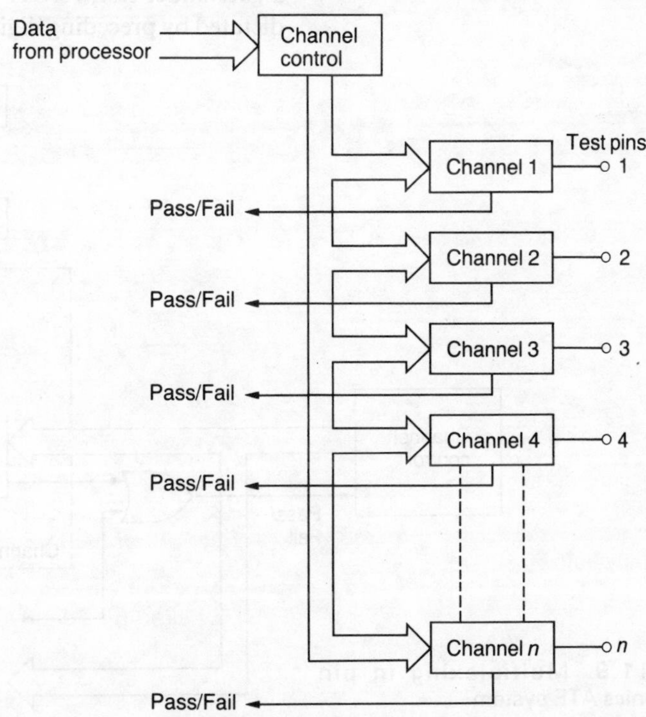

Fig. 11.8 Memory backed pin electronics system

Pin multiplexing

The complexity of modern digital circuit boards results in increasing numbers of nodes and thus an increasing number of test pins and channels. In order to reduce the number of channels, multiplexing may be used, where a single channel is used to control more than one test pin. Figure 11.9 shows a 4-pin multiplexing. Multiplexing is possible for nodes that are independent of one another. Obviously, the more nodes that can be multiplexed to a single channel, the fewer the channels that are required for a given set of nodes and the lower the cost. However, there is a practical limit to this. First, each node of a single DUT must be assigned to a different channel. Secondly, no node in the group of nodes assigned to a channel can have any of the other nodes in the group for any subsequent part of the test programme. The degree of pin multiplexing is determined by the device organization of the board, i.e. the degree to which ICs are interconnected.

Returning to Fig. 11.9, the responses from each channel, i.e. the Pass/Fail indications, are brought together via an OR gate to create a single Pass/Fail line for the test sequence, which is monitored in real time by the channel control.

Stress caused by node-forcing

The in-circuit tester is, in essence, a functional tester for individual devices on a digital board. In doing so, it forces the input nodes of a gate under test, HIGH or LOW, regardless of its normal state dictated by preceding digital devices. This approach is very useful

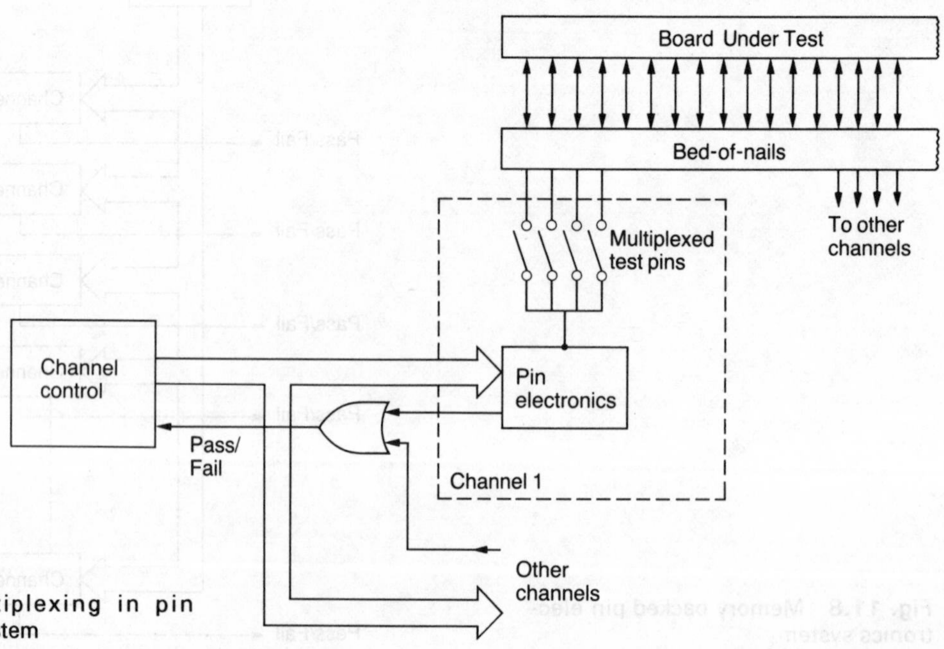

Fig. 11.9 Multiplexing in pin electronics ATE system

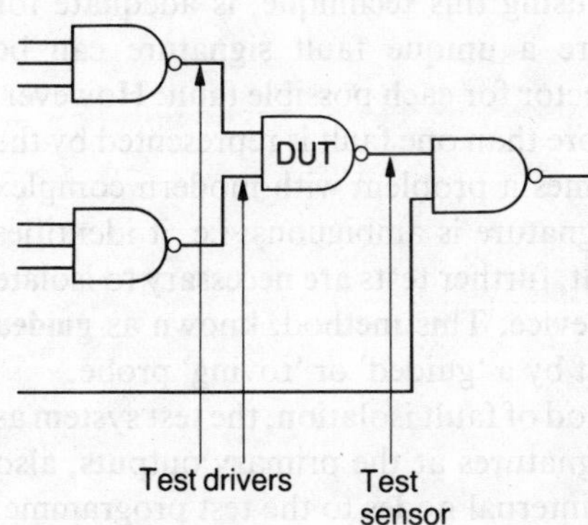

Fig. 11.10 Connection of an In-circuit tester to a NAND gate

in fault diagnosis. However, it may stress a logic device in a manner that is outside of the device's operating specifications. This stress caused by in-circuit testing is known as 'over-driving' or 'backdriving', (already described in Chapter 5).

Figure 11.10 shows the connections for an in-circuit test on a simple NAND gate. Assume that the inputs to the DUT are connected to the output of other logic devices. The DUT is not the one being back-driven or over-driven, but rather some outputs that are electrically connected to the nodes that are being driven (or forced) by the test drivers. Problems arising from backdriving are related to excessive temperature at semi-conductor junctions and bondwires that connect the chip terminals to the package of the IC. Another backdriving problem is related to CMOS chips which may self-destruct if any of its inputs or outputs swing more than about 500 mV above the power supply voltage. These problems may be overcome by limiting each test sequence to a very short period, usually less than 2 ms, and providing a cool down interval between test sequences. Safeguards for various devices are incorporated in a software library, which is called up during the development of a test programme, and these can eliminate all potential damage during the application of the programme.

Digital Board Functional Tester

In-circuit testers are, in reality, in-circuit functional testers which carry out functional tests on individual components on the board. A board functional tester evaluates the performance of the completed printed circuit board, normally via the edge connector. The edge connector provides the tester with access to the primary inputs and outputs of the board. However, if access to internal nodes is required, e.g. for precise fault isolation, it must be achieved via a 'roving' or 'guided' probe or a bed-of-nails.

The most basic use of a board functional ATE is as a Go/No-Go tester to provide a quick Pass/Fail indication. For failed boards, such a test does not locate the faulty component or identify the nature of the fault, both of which are essential for repair purposes and also for improvements in the process of manufacture. To locate these faulty components, further fault isolation procedures must be carried out.

One method for fault isolation is to use the 'fault signature' technique. In this technique, the effect or signature of each fault, as observed at the edge connector, is stored in a memory file. The logic state of each primary output at the edge connector, Low, High, positive or negative pulse, in transition or floating is recorded. To ensure that each fault produces a unique 'fault signature' at the primary outputs, special test stimuli are included in the test programme.

When a No-Go or Fail indication is given, the tester then

compares the state of the primary outputs with those stored in the fault isolation file in order to identify the faulty component or device. This method is known as automatic or immediate fault isolation. Fault coverage, using this technique, is adequate for simple logic boards, where a unique fault signature can be produced at the edge connector for each possible fault. However, fault equivalence, where more than one fault is represented by the same fault signature, becomes a problem with modern complex boards. Where the fault signature is ambiguous, i.e. it identifies more than one possible fault, further tests are necessary to isolate the faulty component or device. This method, known as **guided fault isolation**, is carried out by a 'guided' or 'roving' probe.

In the guided probe method of fault isolation, the test system as well as storing the fault signatures at the primary outputs, also stores the responses of the internal nodes to the test programme. When a faulty board is detected, the tester then instructs the operator to use the probe to check the state of internal nodes in a sequence under the control of the main processor of the test system, until the source of the fault is identified.

Figure 11.11 shows a block diagram of a basic board functional

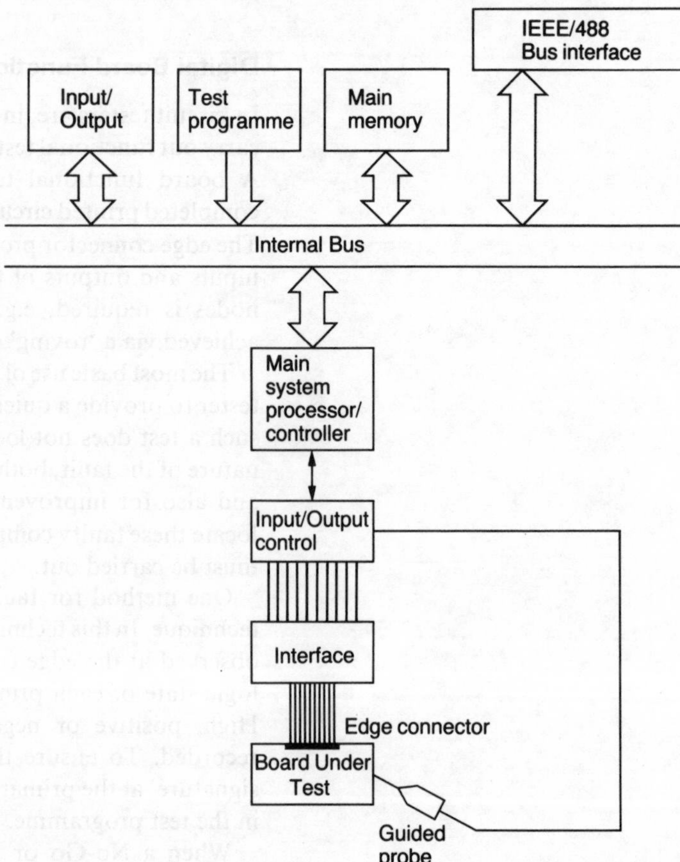

Fig. 11.11 Basic block diagram for a functional tester

automatic test system. The block diagram follows the same principles of other ATE systems. The main processor or computer communicates with the other parts of the system via the internal bus structure. Other peripheral devices may be connected to the system via the IEEE/488 bus interface. The test programme is loaded into the main memory which may contain fault isolation files and procedures. The processor then carries out the test programme by instructing the input/output control of the logic states needed to set the primary inputs of the BUT, i.e. to set the input stimulus. The processor receives the digital responses at the primary outputs, and using the stored test data, indicates Pass or Fail. It may also diagnose the faulty component or device and the nature of the fault by comparing the set of output responses, i.e. the fault signature, with those stored in the fault isolation files. If the precise nature of the fault remains unidentified, the guided probe is then brought into operation. The probe acts as an extra input/output contact. It may be used as a driver or as a sensor under the control of the processor. When further tests are needed to isolate the fault, the processor 'guides' or instructs the operator to test a particular internal node on the BUT by placing the probe at the selected node. The processor, using the probe as an extra driver or sensor, initiates a further test stimulus and monitors the response. If the fault remains unidentified, a further instruction is given to the operator to move the probe to another node, and so on, until the cause of the fault is identified. The purpose is to find the component or device whose input patterns are correct, but whose output pattern is incorrect.

Signature Testing

Signature testing is widely used in both in-current and functional testers. One application of signature testing has already been mentioned, namely the 'fault signature' technique for fault isolation in board functional testing. A test programme consists of a series of test sequences which are applied to the input terminals of a device or a complete board. Each test sequence produces a set of responses at the output terminals. The responses are logic states of '0' or '1', i.e. binary ouput responses. The evaluation of these responses can be carried out individually by the processor to check the function of the device or board. This is time-consuming, occupying a large portion of the processor's time. A more efficient method is to consider the output responses as patterns, i.e. a set of logic or binary states. Consider the simple 2-input NAND gate in Fig. 11.12. As explained earlier in this chapter, a functional test programme involves taking the gate through its truth table. That means feeding the test patterns 0011 and 0101 at inputs N_1 and N_2 respectively, with the expected output response pattern 1110 at N_3.

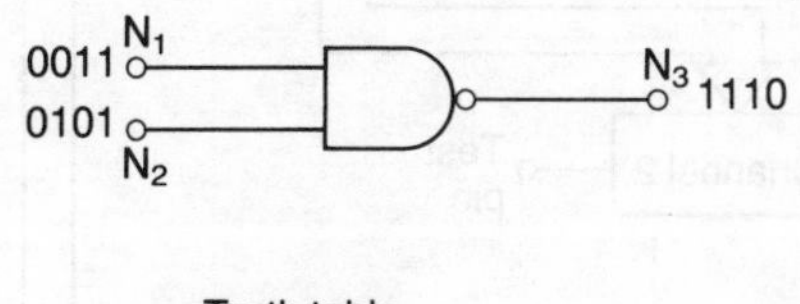

Truth table

N_1	N_2	N_3
0	0	1
0	1	1
1	0	1
1	1	0

Fig. 11.12

The sequence of binary values at the nodes are known as the 'signature' of the node. For the simple test programme under consideration, the binary signatures at N_1, N_2 and N_3 are short enough to be treated without the need for compression. However, in most cases, test programmes are more lengthy and complex, resulting in test patterns containing long strings of zeros and ones. In such cases, the binary signature becomes too cumbersome for easy monitoring, comparison and manipulation. A form of 'compressed' signature is therefore necessary.

There are a number of ways of compressing the data or signature at the output. One method is to count the number of times the state of the node changes from '0' to '1' or '1' to '0' during the test programme. This is known as 'transition counting'. The tester simply counts the number of changes on the output node N_3 and compares this number with the stored correct value.

The disadvantage of this method is that it is possible for a board to contain a fault which alters the binary response signature at the output, but not the 'transition count'.

An alternative and more popular method is the 'cyclic-redundancy-check' (CRC) signature. This is the method used in the signature analyser described in Chapter 7, where the binary string is fed into a feedback shift register to produce a unique compressed signature. The principles of signature testing may be used in cases where a number of output responses have to be tested simultaneously. In this case, a parallel input CRC generator is employed to produce a signature for comparison with that obtained from a known-good board. Figure 11.13 shows the use of signature testing in an in-circuit test system. The test programme may initiate a test sequence of a number of devices, such as gates or

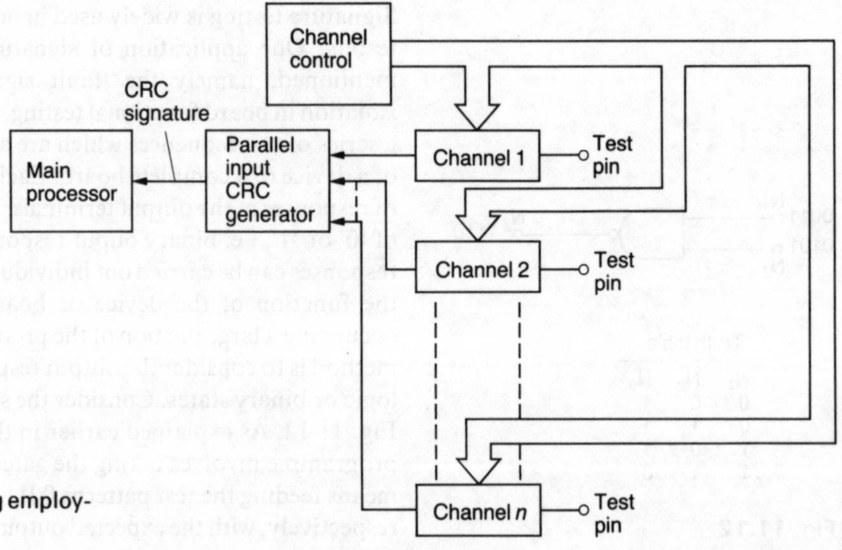

Fig. 11.13 In-circuit testing employing signature analysis

counters, on the board, employing a number of channels and test pins. The responses obtained from each test are fed into the parallel input CRC generator, as shown. The CRC generator produces a single compressed test signature, which is fed into the main processor for comparison and fault detection. The same technique may be used when testing devices with multiple outputs, such as RAMs or ROMs as we shall see in Chapter 12.

Simulation

The generation of test patterns and test programmes is only the first step in the testing process. Before applying the programme to actual faulty boards, its effectiveness must be evaluated to find out its fault coverage expressed as a percentage of the faults in the fault list. There are two techniques used to evaluate the test programmes. The first is to insert actual faults on to a known-good board and then run the programme to determine if it can detect the inserted fault. This is then repeated for all the faults in the fault list. This method is a simple way of evaluating the effectiveness of a test programme. However, it suffers from a number of drawbacks, including:

(a) that some faults, e.g. propagation delay faults, cannot be inserted physically on to a board,
(b) that stuck-at faults may damage TTL devices, e.g. pulling the output of a TTL gate to +5 V for long enough to damage the gate, and
(c) this method requires a good working board which means that test evaluation can only begin after the design and prototype stages have been completed.

A second, and more universally used technique, is fault simulation. In this method, the tester simulates the expected output responses of the BUT, i.e. produces signals which are the same as those produced by the BUT when stimulated by a particular input test pattern. To do this, a logic simulator has to be included in the automatic test equipment. The logic simulator must first produce a circuit model. The circuit description, connections and devices used, are fed into the simulator. The simulator is also provided with a 'device library' which consists of models of behaviour of a range of standard commercial or in-house devices. With the use of this library, the simulator creates a circuit model of the board. This model can be tested in just the same way as a real circuit. With such a model, the simulator can produce a set of output responses expected from the board when working normally, or with any fault from the fault list.

The use of simulators is not limited to the testing process. They can be used to verify the initial design and help in PCB layout. They are used simultaneously with the design process. As far as testing is concerned, logic simulators reduce test programme generation and execution times and improve fault isolation and detection capabilities. Test evaluation, using simulators, can begin before the design stage is completed.

12 Testing LSI boards

So far, testing techniques for digital boards based on logic patterns have been considered, which provide information about their truth tables. Other patterns may be used for determining more data about faults. These techniques are adequate for boards containing 40 to 80 components and devices, mainly of small to medium scale integration (SSI and MSI). The advent of Large Scale Integration (LSI) and Very Large Scale Integration (VLSI) has created new challenges when testing digital boards. Test patterns of '0's and '1's only are no longer suitable. LSI devices have bus-structured boards with the various units communicating with each other by writing and reading 'words' on a digital bus. Testing bus-structured boards requires a different test strategy than that employed for conventional digital boards, both in terms of testing the LSI/VLSI devices themselves, as well as in testing the complete board.

Bus-structured boards may be a complete microcomputer system with a microprocessor chip, RAM and ROM memory chips, as well as other specialized LSI devices, or it may contain only parts of a system. In order to develop a test strategy for bus-structured boards, the types of faults likely to occur on such boards must be considered.

Types of Faults

Faults on a bus-structured board may be divided into three categories:

Assembly faults

These faults are caused by assembly operators' mistakes. These include wrong components, open and short circuits, components incorrectly connected, and catastrophic component failures. These are faults found in other types of printed circuit boards and are not unique to LSI/VLSI boards. They manifest themselves as 'stuck-at' faults, not dissimilar to conventional digital boards.

'Hard' chip faults

They are the type of fault caused by a failure of a logic element within the LSI/VLSI device itself. Unlike assembly faults, this type of fault manifests itself normally as a 'stuck-at' fault at either the device's input or output when the LSI/VLSI device is operating. 'Hard' faults are repeatable faults, always manifesting themselves in the same way.

'Soft' chip faults

Most LSI/VLSI chip faults do not manifest themselves as 'stuck-at' faults. The complexity of such devices is such that a number of faults may occur which are related to the data pattern used (pattern sensitive faults), the speed of the clock, and propagation delays (timing interaction faults). Such faults, known as 'soft' faults, are not necessarily repeatable and their occurrence is generally random. They are influenced by the chip 'environment' on the board, e.g. noise, power rails and electric and magnetic fields. 'Soft' faults can only be detected by a functional test on the board, which closely resembles the conditions of the final product at the speed at which the board is intended to operate.

Testing Techniques

A test strategy for bus-structured board must be capable of identifying all types of faults that may be present on the board. Each type of fault requires a specific technique to diagnose.

Diagnosing assembly faults

As stated earlier, assembly errors manifest themselves as 'stuck-at' faults. In principle, finding these faults is not difficult. A node fails to change its logic state when forced by the tester. A test programme is written which will, via an edge connector interface, exercise all nodes on the board. The responses are then compared with those obtained from a known-good board to detect the presence of a fault. This is the same as the method employed for SSI/MSI digital board. In the case of LSI/VLSI boards, the complexity of the devices requires more complicated and longer test patterns to fully test all the nodes. A simple test programme to check the bus lines is the 'free run' technique. Here the microprocessor is separated from the other units, e.g. by removing the devices, and then forcing in an instruction such as No-operation (NOP) that will cause the microprocessor to repeatedly increment the address lines. The microprocessor will scan through the whole address field. A cyclic-redundancy-check (CRC), check-run or signature of the address field may be obtained to verify the address lines. The same process may be repeated with other devices reconnected back one at a time. A free-run test can take a long time and does not necessarily exercise all the nodes on the board. To do this, other more sophisticated test programmes must be used. These must provide facilities for easily programming these patterns, without tedious repetition and must also be capable of generating and receiving test patterns containing a lot of data.

A problem peculiar to bus-structured boards is that of identifying the faulty device causing the 'stuck-at' fault at a node. In a bus-structured board, the inputs and outputs of all devices are connected to the same bus structure. The problem, therefore, is to locate the fault 'beyond the node'. Figure 12.1 shows a typical LSI board containing a microprocessor, RAM and ROM memory

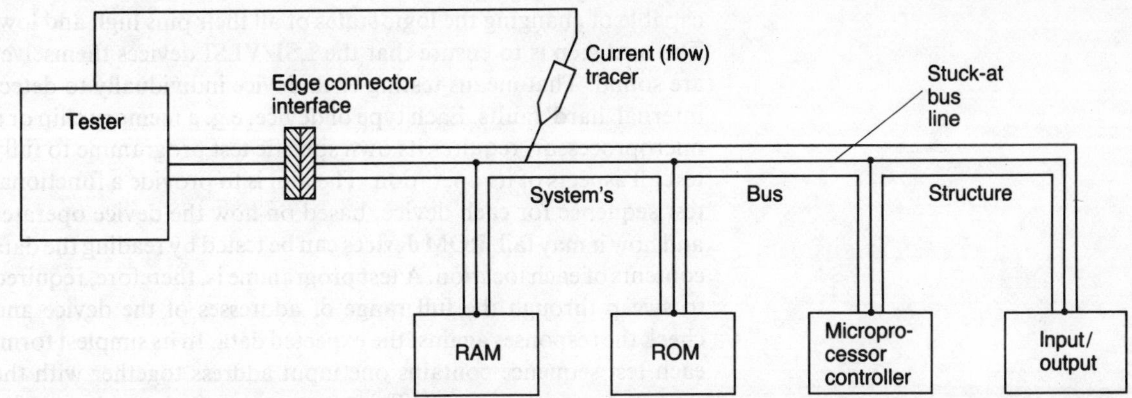

Fig. 12.1 Testing a LSI board

chips, as well as an input/output unit. The tester is connected to the board via an edge connector interface providing access to the system's bus structure. The bus shown includes the data, address and control lines. The tester, in carrying out the test programme, may detect a stuck-at fault on a bus line. The cause of the fault could be the bus line itself or any other chip connected to it. Added to this is the problem of the bi-directional bus with data flowing to various different components in the course of the test programme. The bi-directional bus is, in effect, a feed-back loop which introduces the further problem of separating the cause and the effect of the fault symptom. The tester generates test stimuli, analyses test data and diagnoses the cause of the fault. The guided probe technique remains applicable for diagnosing assembly faults. However, LSI/VLSI boards demand a more sophisticated guided probe technique for successful fault diagnosis at normal operating speeds. One solution to the problems occurring in LSI/VLSI boards is to use 'current probing' techniques. A current pulser, together with a current tracer, may be used to identify the precise cause of the 'stuck-at' fault observed on a bus line. Some

ATE systems provide such probes which may be used by the operator under guidance provided by the tester to trace the 'sink' or 'source' of a current on the bus. The method used is the same as that explained in Chapter 5. The current pulser probe is placed on to the faulty bus line to provide a pulsating current along the bus line. The current tracer probe is then moved along a path that keeps the current indication on the probe constant until the cause of the fault is found.

Diagnosing 'hard' chip faults

The tests carried out to identify assembly faults verify the board interconnections, namely that all SSI and MSI logic circuits are functioning correctly, and that LSI and VLSI devices are at least capable of changing the logic states of all their pins high and low. The next step is to ensure that the LSI/VLSI devices themselves are sound. That means testing each device individually to detect internal 'hard' faults. Each type of device, e.g. a memory chip or a microprocessor, requires its own specific test programme to fully test all aspects of its operation. The aim is to provide a functional test sequence for each device, based on how the device operates and how it may fail. **ROM devices** can be tested by reading the data contents of each location. A test programme is, therefore, required to sweep through the full range of addresses of the device and check the responses against the expected data. In its simplest form, each test sequence contains one input address together with the expected output response. This test sequence is then repeated for each address location of the device. The test programme may be shortened by the use of data compression techniques of the output responses. The output responses, i.e. the contents of all locations, are added together to produce a signature; either a binary or a CRC signature, which the tester then uses to compare with that produced by a known-good ROM. Figure 12.2 shows a ROM with address locations 0800-OFFF under test. The tester generates the range of addresses starting at base address 0800 and finishing at OFFF. These addresses are fed one at a time to the input of the ROM device and the responses fed into the CRC signature generator. The signature generator produces what is known as a 'checksum' of the responses, which is normally a 4-digit hexadecimal number. This checksum is then compared with the expected checksum of the device and a Pass/Fail indication is given.

For **RAM devices**, the minimum recommended test is to write and read back a '1' or a '0' from each cell in the memory. This is carried out by a test programme which sweeps through the address range of the RAM device writing and reading data at each memory location. There are a number of strategies to be followed in testing RAM devices, determined by the pattern of '1's and '0's written

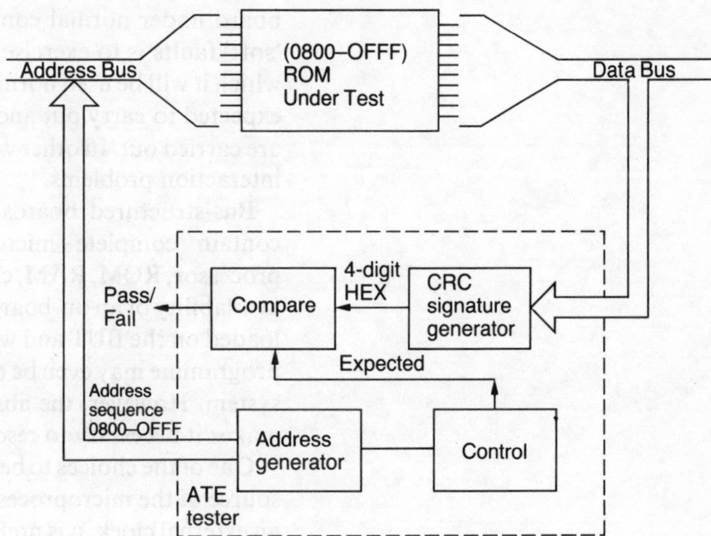

Fig. 12.2 Testing ROM chips

and read into the memory locations. The simplest strategy is the Write/Read pattern which writes a '1' in one location then reads it to check that it is a '1'. It then writes '1' in the next location and so on. The whole process is then repeated with logic '0' instead of '1'. Such a pattern, however, fails to detect a number of possible faults, including incorrect addressing, due to decoder malfunction. Other patterns used are the 'chequerboard' pattern which writes alternate '1's and '0's in the memory cells, the diagonal pattern, the marching pattern (where a 1 or a 0 is continuously shifted from one memory cell to the next) and the more complex galloping pattern. For a **microprocessor**, the minimum test requirement is to execute every instruction once and normally more than once. A full test of a microprocessor device is long and complex. It includes checking every part of its architecture such as the ALU, the programme counter, the various registers, decoders, and buffers. Such tests are standard which are generated by subroutines relating to the particular microprocessor-under-test.

A number of the test sequences carried out for detecting 'hard' faults can be stored in ROM on the BUT. The stored programme may be used for self-testing purposes, e.g. when switching on or to form part of the test programme carried out by an ATE tester. The regularity of some of the tests, those for ROM and the microprocessor for example, makes this method very popular, provided there is the memory space available.

Diagnosing 'soft' faults

'Soft' faults manifest themselves when the board is in operation. A device on the BUT may show no assembly or hard faults, yet can display a fault when in interaction with the other devices on the board under normal conditions. The only acceptable check for 'soft' faults is to exercise the board in modes similar to those in which it will be used normally, both in terms of the operations it is expected to carry out and the speed with which these operations are carried out. In other words, a **real-time, real-life** test to identify interaction problems.

Bus-structured boards may be of various types. Often they contain complete microcomputer systems including microprocessor, ROM, RAM, clock generator and peripheral chips. The availability of an on-board RAM allows the test programme to be loaded on the BUT and with an on-board microprocessor the test programme may even be executed with little support from the test system. However, the absence of these elements from the board makes it necessary to resort to an external test system.

One of the choices to be made in testing a LSI/VLSI board is the source of the microprocessor clock. In a board designed to accept an external clock, it is preferable that a faster, more precisely timed test speed is obtained by driving the on-board microprocessor from the test-system clock. An alternative is to allow the microprocessor to operate from the on-board clock which ensures 'real life' conditions. If this option is chosen, the test system must be synchronized with the on-board clock.

Initialization

Automatic testing and diagnosis relies on the comparison of the device or board responses to particular stimuli with those obtained from a good board when fed with the same stimuli. The responses obtained from any device or board depend on (a) the stimulus applied, and (b) the initial state of the device or board before the stimulus signals are applied. Therefore, for viable response comparisons to be made, both the stimulus signals, as well as the initial state of the devices or boards, must be identical. This applies equally to testing devices for 'hard' faults and testing complete boards for 'soft' faults. The first part of a functional test programme is, therefore, designed to 'initialise' the device or BUT to establish a common background to the test programme. Initialization may be carried out externally by the tester or may be built into the on-board ROM which is recalled when the board is placed under test.

Test Strategy

There is no single test strategy that may be followed in testing every bus-structured board. The manner in which the various tests are carried out and the fault coverage of these tests depend on the type of BUT (e.g. the type of LSI/VLSI devices used), the function the board is expected to carry out when it is connected to the final system, and, of course, the cost of the tests. Underlining all this is the access to the board by the tester.

Access to the BUT is an important factor in determining the type of strategy and test programme employed. Some boards are designed for easy access by the tester to the board via the edge connector or a test connector. In some cases, access is achieved by unplugging the microprocessor and substituting a corresponding pod, thus gaining access to all the bus lines. In this case, another method of access is required for testing the microprocessor itself. A convenient way of connecting the tester to the bus is to place a Dual in-line (DIL) clip over the microprocessor while it is still on the board. The tester may then halt the microprocessor and take complete control of the bus, or it may control the microprocessor itself to carry out certain tests.

Table 12.1 shows a general-purpose test strategy for bus-structured boards with an on-board microprocessor.

Table 12.1

Test No.	*Faults covered*
1. Isolate all devices from the buses including the microprocessor. Force bus lines High and Low. Use appropriate methods for diagnosis 'beyond the node'.	Detects SSI/MSI logic and stuck-at faults, short and open circuits, bridging, faults on bus lines and ICs.
2. Isolate microprocessor. Test other devices individually for 'hard' chip faults.	Detects such things as faulty ROM, RAM, buffer, clock and PIO.
3. Isolate all devices. Reinstate and initialize microprocessor. Carry out microprocessor instruction and architecture tests.	Detects microprocessor 'hard' faults.
4. Reinstate all devices. Carry out a full board function test at operational or higher speeds.	Detects 'soft' faults in microprocessor and other devices.

Test 1. Testing the buses

Isolating devices from the bus may be achieved mechanically by removing the chips themselves or by opening the bus using dip switches or jumper wires. Isolation may also be achieved electrically by placing each bus buffer at its high impedance (tristate) mode. The test for the bus consists of a check to show that each line can be 'pulled' High and Low. This test should also include a check on SSI/MSI logic devices to identify 'stuck-at' faults.

Where a bus-line fault is identified, detection and fault diagnosis beyond the node must be carried out to identify the cause of the fault, as explained earlier. Where device isolation is achieved by placing the buffers in tristate, a bus-line fault could also mean a buffer fault, which must also be investigated.

Test 2. Testing LSI/VLSI devices

Microprocessor isolation may be achieved by physically removing the chip or by placing it into a tristate mode. In this test, the tester takes complete control of the three buses (address, data and control), and carries out systematic testing of each device individually. As each device is tested and passed, it can be used to assist in the testing of subsequent devices. In this way, interaction between the various devices can be tested, which allows detection of some timing faults.

Test 3. Testing the microprocessor

All devices are disconnected from the bus except for the microprocessor. The tester then exercises the microprocessor through its instruction set and checks its architecture. It is normal that the tested devices play a part in testing the microprocessor itself by using, for instance, the on-board RAM and ROM. Essentially, this is a slow speed test (single-step operation is not unusual), since it is mainly concerned with verifying micro-processor instructions. However, real-time tests may be carried out to detect some internal microprocessor timing problems.

Test 4. Real-time testing of the board

This is a real-time test of the functions of the complete board. The board will be tested under as near working conditions as possible. The most difficult problem in this test is to actually isolate the cause of the fault. Sophisticated diagnostic aids, including automatic guided probes, digitizing oscilloscopes and logic analysers, may have to be employed to diagnose the source of failure.

13 Trends in instruments and testing

Electronic manufacturing techniques have been changing dramatically in the past few years. The different manufacturing methods, the introduction of new and more complex devices and the increasing use of VLSI chips bring with them new demands for testing equipment and strategies. All aspects of testing from the humble DVM to the functional tester are continously assessed and developed to meet the new demand created by new processes and customer requirements.

The advance in electronic PCB manufacture will follow many avenues and trends, all of which will be integrated to develop new manufacturing processes and techniques. Two related trends that underpin future development are the advances made in LSI and VLSI chips and surface-mounted-technology, (SMT). Experts in industry predict that the 1990s will see the introduction of sub-assemblies containing 200–500 pin devices with 60 000 to 80 000 equivalent gates. Module gate-to-pin ratio which has grown from 12:1 to 150:1 in recent years will, by about 1990, exceed 320:1. Beyond this, there will be the 25×25 matrices, (a total of 625 pins), giving 200 000 equivalent gate modules. These developments will create new testing challenges. Merely getting access to the device pin will present problems. Many future electronic products will consist of 'functional modules', i.e. sub-assemblies containing as much logic as today's systems. In the 90's such modules will include the 32-bit microprocessor, the 1 megabit RAM's and ROM's, and other programmable logic devices built upon a new bus structure to accommodate the expanded word length. Beyond that, sub-assembly modules will contain multiple 32-bit microprocessor, 4–16 megabit RAM's, voice activated transreceivers and a variety of bussing systems and new standard bus connectors.

Built-in test

To counter the effects of the above mentioned trends, attention is being turned to the use of built-in tests, (BIT), techniques. The aim is to use additional circuitry to incorporate some of the test procedures into the UUT. Modern technology makes it possible to include this additional circuitry at low cost. BIT may be used to detect and isolate a faulty component in the UUT directly or it may be employed to assist external test equipment.

In logic circuits, BIT is incorporated by the use of built-in-test-equipment, (BITE). Blocks are designed to generate the appropriate patterns, capture and test for responses, using data compression techniques such as signature analysis. An example of BITE is the built-in logic block observer, (BILBO). A BILBO is a multi-purpose test module which can function in two basic modes: as an input test pattern generator or as an output signature register. It consists of a number of bistables, (flip flops), and gates for shift and feedback operations. One or more BILBO's may be used in BIT circuitry together with decoders and fault indicators. BILBO is a very versatile building block for constructing self-testing circuitry or simply for improving the ease of testing by conventional techniques.

For microprocessor circuits, a different technique is used which takes advantage of their computing power. Two software programmes are included in ROM: the programme required for normal operation and a test programme. The test programme may be selected by a test control input to the circuit under test. When the test control is 'off' the circuit performs in its normal fashion. When the test control is 'on', the microprocessor carries out the set of instructions contained in the test programme for checking its own operation and that of the other units and the system itself. BIT programmes may be based on two different techniques. The first is the 'bootstrap' technique, where each microprocessor instruction is tested separately and also to check the response of the system to these instructions. The second technique is known as the architectural-checkout which first tests the architecture of the microprocessor itself, starting with the programme counter. It then proceeds to test the other system units such as ROM, RAM and interfaces. Although some of the test problems may be resolved by improved design and imaginative layout, the use of built-in test circuitry is destined to increase rapidly. This is particularly so with the multiplicity of logical- and microprocessor-controlled equipment being manufactured for industry and for the home, in an effort to reduce maintenance costs.

The fast developing surface mounted technology of components and devices is introducing new developments in design and testing techniques. The effect of SMT is (a) the introduction of very small components and devices, (b) increasing component density, (c) smaller boards and (d) the instruction of the leadless component. For example surface mounted capacitors measure 3.63 × 1.8 × 1.35 mm for values up to 100 μF and 20-way connectors measure 34 × 7 mm with an overall height of 13 mm. Vast reductions in space for devices (LSI & VLSI) can be achieved using surface-mounted techniques.

The miniaturized and dense-printed circuit board, employing surface mounted components and devices, make adequate board testing difficult, but no less essential. Very small contact probes are necessary to ensure no short circuiting of test nodes by the probe. Close inspection of contacts and joints in surface mounted boards is not possible by the naked eye or even with the use of a simple magnifying glass. Microscopes or high resolution RGB video systems and colour monitors, together with adjustable inspection platforms for tilting the board to make observations at different angles, are necessary.

Trends in ATE

Automatic testing has to develop in line with changing manufacturing processes. The emphasis is likely to remain on quality, cost-effective testing and the need to reduce failure rates. In an effort to reduce costs, 'fault prevention' is to replace 'fault detection' as the overriding test strategy. An example of such a strategy is a board-test programme containing a real-time alarm which can halt an assembly process if a number of consecutive boards exhibit the same fault. The increasing use of automatic assembly facilities and machine visual inspection since traditional board test strategy employing in-circuit and functional testing unnecessarily costly.

The debate between the advocates of in-circuit testing on the one hand and functional testing on the other as the best test strategy, is likely to continue more out of loyalty to a firm or manufacturer than to objective facts. In-circuit testing, once the favourite of PCB manufacturers, has increasingly come under question with new surface mounted devices, (SMD), being manufactured. New surface mounted technology, (SMT), is introducing smaller devices geometry making the use of a bed-of-nails fixture very difficult. Complex parts require longer test times introducing real dangers of damage to other devices due to backdriving. Component density introduce additional problems of screening.

Functional testing is used to identify more complex faults. In order to identify faulty components, it requires a lengthy programme as well as a roving probe. Improvements in board testability by bringing more test nodes to the edge connector has brought about some improvements in the diagnostic capabilities of the functional tester.

A combination of both types of testers is being introduced by manufacturers as an alternative to the two separate test strategies. Such testers, known as **combinational testers** combine the testing capabilities of both in-circuit and functional testing machines. They provide very high fault coverage and yield, while they overcome many of the drawbacks of the other test type machines. Combitional testers introduce a flexibility that did not exist previously. It is well known that fault occurrences, both in terms of number and frequency, change as the production process develops. The test strategy used at the beginning of any new production process, is not necessarily the most suitable one for use at a later period, when the production process has 'matured' and stabilized. A change of strategy is desirable at specific periods of time and may be achieved smoothly with a combinational tester.

The use of microprocessors

Over the past few years there has been a steady growth in the use of microprocessors in instruments, enabling the facia to change from a cluttering of switches and potentiometers to a much cleaner and clearer set of controls, in the form of push buttons and key pads. New facilities are being offered by such instruments previously reserved for very expensive and specialised equipment.

Self calibration and self-check capabilities are being incorporated in almost all test instruments. A self-test programme is initiated by the microprocessor at switch-on. Such a programme will typically exercise all functional blocks of the instrument to verify the proper interaction between the blocks, the microprocessor, RAM, ROM, input/output units and video display.

On-screen menu has become a general feature of test instruments, making the equipment 'user friendly'. The menu displays the available measuring option and provides instructions as to which key should be pressed to select the required mode. Touch sensitive screens may be provided, rendering the selection virtually idiot-proof by merely touching a marked square on the VDU. Such developments have made it possible for operators with little skill and knowledge to use sophisticated instruments, such as logic analysers and digitizing oscilloscopes.

The use of microcomputers with added-on facilities is introducing a new generation of instruments called the multi-purpose instrument. Logic analysers, for instance, can incorporate data acquisition, data storage, data generation and data processing. Oscilloscopes and logic analysers are combined, making them capable of capturing multi-channel input data.

Artificial intelligence (AI)

Artificial intelligence is the study of concepts and techniques, enabling computers to do tasks that are associated with human intelligence, such as an ability to reason. The potential of artificial intelligence in the production process is increasingly being recognized and realized. Image analysis, pattern recognition and scene analysis are being employed for automated test and inspection systems.

Display technology

Advances in display technology have been slow to develop. The traditional CRT remains the most versatile and reliable VDU, keeping the old thermionic technology alive. The 3-gun, (RGB), colour tube suffers from lack of picture definition due to the limitations imposed by the shadow mask. It also lacks in colour integrity at the extremities of the screen. Further, it represents a complex manufacturing process which adds to the cost of the tube.

A number of possible improvements have been developed by the manufacturers. One such development is to use a normal monochrome tube with a high-speed liquid crystal 'shutter' which selects the appropriate primary colour. The shutter displays each line via a different filter to produce a subjective colour display. Other display technologies have also been developed with the purpose of producing a flat screen that can replace the CRT.

In the liquid-crystal technology field, the development of crystals with memory properties is leading to the flat panel video display. These crystals can be switched into a dark or a light state by electronic signals. Once switched, the crystals remain in that state until re-addressed. A matrix of 1000 × 1000 dots, (a total of one million dots or picture elements), may be employed for a fully versatile video screen.

Testability

The increasing cost of production testing has led to the concept of 'test influenced design' or 'design for testability'. A great deal of time and money can be saved by taking a little extra care during the design stage of a PCB. With the new surface mounted technology being increasingly employed in PCB manufacture, building in testability is becoming essential. Improved testability is achieved by incorporating a facility to disable all on-board clocks and lay-out design is improved by providing access to circuit nodes from one side of the PCB.

Appendix
Logic gate symbols

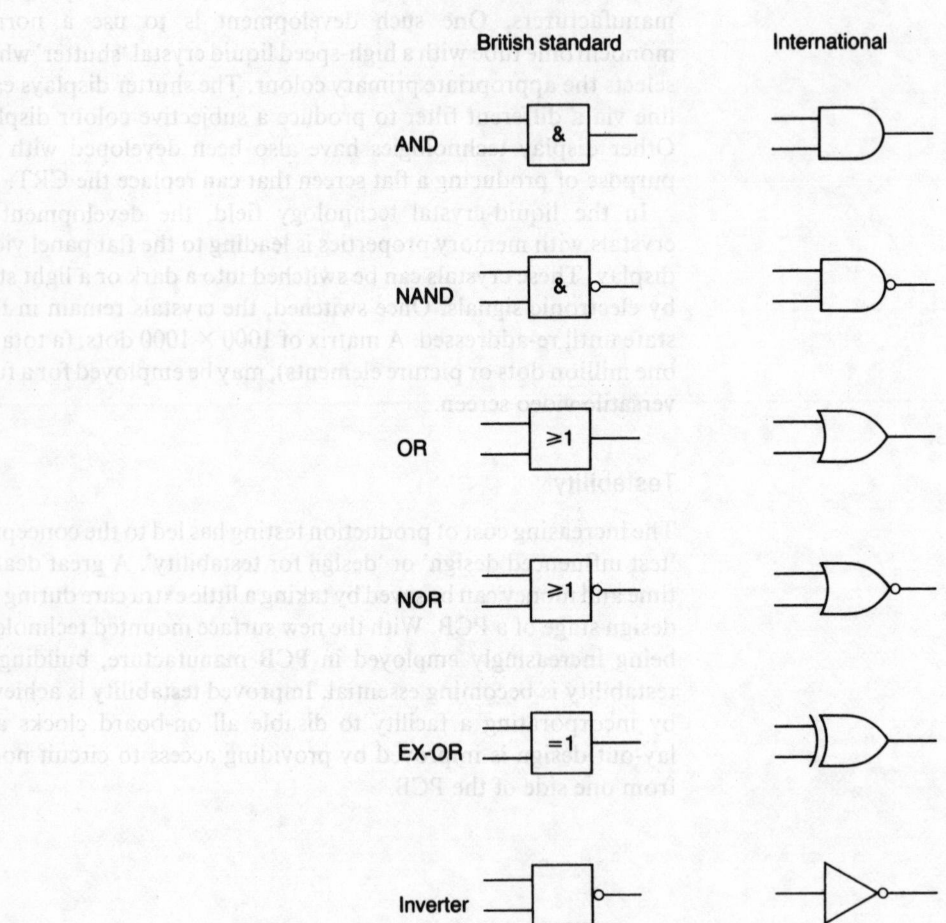

Index